AS-Level Physics

The Revision Guide

Exam Board: Edexcel

Editors:
Amy Boutal, Julie Wakeling, Sarah Williams

Contributors
Tony Alldridge, Jane Cartwright, Peter Cecil, Mark A. Edwards, Barbara Mascetti, John Myers, Andy Williams

Proofreader:
Glenn Rogers

Published by Coordination Group Publications Ltd.

Data used to construct stopping distance diagram on page 20 from the Highway Code.
Reproduced under the terms of the Click-Use Licence.

With thanks to Jan Greenway for the copyright research.

ISBN: 978 1 84762 129 0

Groovy website: www.cgpbooks.co.uk
Jolly bits of clipart from CorelDRAW®
Printed by Elanders Ltd, Newcastle upon Tyne.

Based on the classic CGP style created by Richard Parsons.

Contents

How Science Works

Unit 1: Section 1 — Mechanics

Unit 1: Section 2 — Materials

Unit 2: Section 1 — Waves

Unit 2: Section 2 — DC Electricity

Unit 2: Section 3 — The Nature of Light

Answering Experiment Questions

The Scientific Process

'How Science Works' is all about the scientific process — how we develop and test scientific ideas. It's what scientists do all day, every day (well, except at coffee time — never come between a scientist and their coffee).

Scientists Come Up with **Theories** — Then **Test Them**...

Science tries to explain **how** and **why** things happen — it **answers questions**. It's all about seeking and gaining **knowledge** about the world around us. Scientists do this by **asking** questions and **suggesting** answers and then **testing** them, to see if they're correct — this is the **scientific process**.

1) **Ask** a question — make an **observation** and ask **why or how** it happens. E.g. what is the nature of light?
2) **Suggest** an answer, or part of an answer, by forming:
   - a **theory** (a possible **explanation** of the observations) e.g. light is a wave.
   - a **model** (a **simplified picture** of what's physically going on)
3) Make a **prediction** or **hypothesis** — a **specific testable statement**, based on the theory, about what will happen in a test situation. E.g. light should interfere and diffract.
4) Carry out a **test** — to provide **evidence** that will support the prediction, or help disprove it. E.g. Young's double-slit experiment.

The evidence supported Quentin's Theory of Flammable Burps.

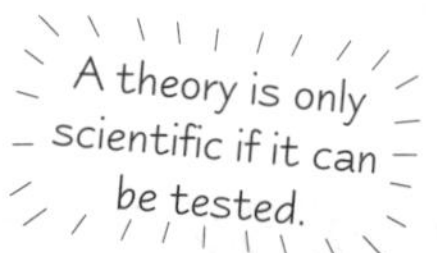

...Then They **Tell** Everyone About Their **Results**...

The results are **published** — scientists need to let others know about their work. Scientists publish their results in **scientific journals**. These are just like normal magazines, only they contain **scientific reports** (called papers) instead of the latest celebrity gossip.

1) Scientific reports are similar to the **lab write-ups** you do in school. And just as a lab write-up is **reviewed** (marked) by your teacher, reports in scientific journals undergo **peer review** before they're published.
2) The report is sent out to **peers** — other scientists that are experts in the **same area**. They examine the data and results, and if they think that the conclusion is reasonable it's **published**. This makes sure that work published in scientific journals is of a **good standard**.
3) But peer review **can't guarantee** the science is **correct** — other scientists still need to **reproduce** it.
4) Sometimes **mistakes** are made and bad work is published. Peer review **isn't perfect** but it's probably the best way for scientists to self-regulate their work and to publish **quality reports**.

...Then **Other Scientists** Will **Test** the Theory Too

Other scientists read the published theories and results, and try to **test the theory** themselves. This involves:

- Repeating the **exact same experiments**.
- Using the theory to make **new predictions** and then testing them with **new experiments**.

If the **Evidence** Supports a Theory, It's **Accepted — for Now**

1) If all the experiments in all the world provide evidence to back it up, the theory is thought of as **scientific 'fact'** (for now).
2) But they never become **totally undisputable** fact. Scientific **breakthroughs or advances** could provide new ways to question and test the theory, which could lead to **new evidence** that **conflicts** with the current evidence. Then the testing starts all over again...

And this, my friend, is the **tentative nature of scientific knowledge** — it's always **changing** and **evolving**.

The Scientific Process

So scientists need evidence to back up their theories. They get it by carrying out experiments, and when that's not possible they carry out studies. But why bother with science at all? We want to know as much as possible so we can use it to try and improve our lives (and because we're nosey).

Evidence Comes From **Controlled Lab Experiments**...

1) Results from **controlled experiments** in **laboratories** are **great**.
2) A lab is the easiest place to **control variables** so that they're all **kept constant** (except for the one you're investigating).

For example, finding the resistance of a piece of material by altering the voltage across the material and measuring the current flowing through it (see p. 46). All other variables need to be kept the same, e.g. the dimensions of the piece of material being tested, as they may also affect its resistance.

... That You can Draw **Meaningful Conclusions** From

1) You always need to make your experiments as **controlled** as possible so you can be confident that any effects you see are linked to the variable you're changing.
2) If you do find a relationship, you need to be careful what you conclude. You need to decide whether the effect you're seeing is **caused** by changing a variable, or whether the two are just **correlated**.

"Right Geoff, you can start the experiment now... I've stopped time..."

Society **Makes Decisions** Based on **Scientific Evidence**

1) Lots of scientific work eventually leads to **important discoveries** or breakthroughs that could **benefit humankind**.
2) These results are **used by society** (that's you, me and everyone else) to **make decisions** — about the way we live, what we eat, what we drive, etc.
3) All sections of society use scientific evidence to make decisions, e.g. politicians use it to devise policies and individuals use science to make decisions about their own lives.

Other factors can **influence** decisions about science or the way science is used:

Economic factors

- Society has to consider the **cost** of implementing changes based on scientific conclusions — e.g. the cost of reducing the UK's carbon emissions to limit the human contribution to **global warming**.
- Scientific research is often **expensive**. E.g. in areas such as astronomy, the Government has to **justify** spending money on a new telescope rather than pumping money into, say, the **NHS** or **schools**.

Social factors

- **Decisions** affect **people's lives** — e.g. when looking for a site to build a **nuclear power station**, you need to consider how it would affect the lives of the people in the **surrounding area**.

Environmental factors

- Many scientists suggest that building **wind farms** would be a **cheap** and **environmentally friendly** way to generate electricity in the future. But some people think that because **wind turbines** can **harm wildlife** such as birds and bats, other methods of generating electricity should be used.

So there you have it — how science works...

Hopefully these pages have given you a nice intro to how science works, e.g. what scientists do to provide you with 'facts'. You need to understand this, as you're expected to know how science works yourself — for the exam and for life.

Scalars and Vectors

Mechanics is one of those things that you either love or hate. I won't tell you which side of the fence I'm on.

Scalars Only Have Size, but Vectors Have Size and Direction

1) A **scalar** has **no direction** — it's **just an amount** of something, like the **mass** of a **sack of meaty dog food**.
2) A **vector** has magnitude (**size**) and **direction** — like the **speed and direction** of next door's **cat** running away.
3) **Force** and **velocity** are both **vectors** — you need to know **which way** they're going as well as **how big** they are.
4) Here are a few examples to get you started:

Scalars	Vectors
mass, temperature, time, length, speed, energy	displacement, force, velocity, acceleration, momentum

Adding Vectors Involves Pythagoras and Trigonometry

Adding two or more vectors is called finding the **resultant** of them.
You find the resultant of two vectors by drawing them '**tip-to-tail**'.

Example Jemima goes for a walk. She walks 3 m North and 4 m East. She has walked 7 m but she isn't 7 m from her starting point. Find the magnitude and direction of her displacement.

Jemima's 'displacement' gives her position relative to her starting point.

First, draw the vectors **tip-to-tail**. Then draw a line from the **tail** of the first vector to the **tip** of the last vector to give the **resultant**:
Because the vectors are at right angles, you get the **magnitude** of the resultant using Pythagoras:

$R^2 = 3^2 + 4^2 = 25$
So $R = 5$ m

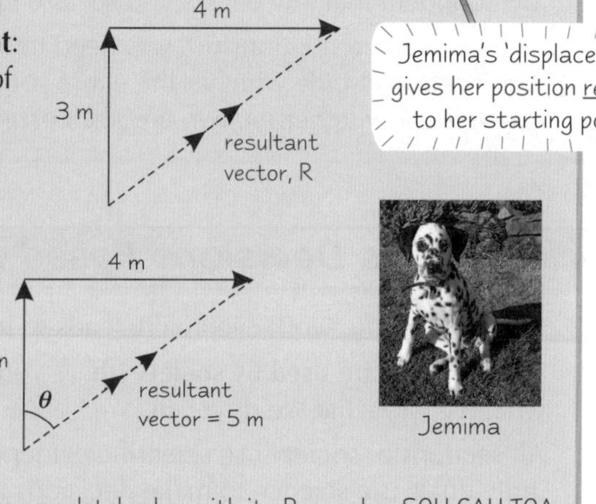

Jemima

Now find the **bearing** of Jemima's new position from her original position.

You use the triangle again, but this time you need to use trigonometry. You know the opposite and the adjacent sides, so you need to use:

$\tan\theta = 4/3$

$\theta = 53.1°$ Trig's really useful in mechanics — so make sure you're completely okay with it. Remember SOH CAH TOA.

Use the Same Method for Resultant Forces or Velocities

If the vectors aren't at right angles, you'll need to do a scale drawing.

Always start by drawing a diagram.

Example

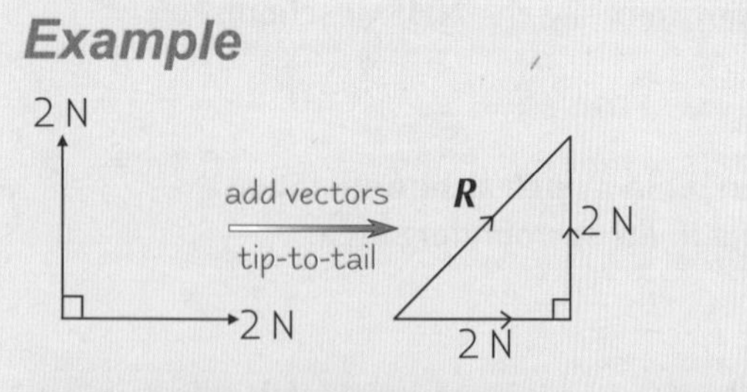

You know the resultant force is at 45° to the horizontal (since both forces are the same size).
So all you need to do is use Pythagoras:

$R^2 = 2^2 + 2^2 = 8$

which gives $R = 2.83$ N at 45° to the horizontal.

Don't forget to take the square root.

Example

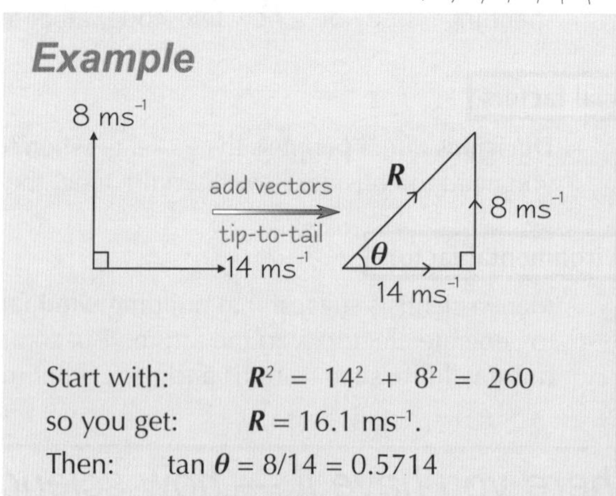

Start with: $R^2 = 14^2 + 8^2 = 260$

so you get: $R = 16.1\ \text{ms}^{-1}$.

Then: $\tan\theta = 8/14 = 0.5714$

$\theta = 29.7°$

Scalars and Vectors

Sometimes you have to do it backwards.

It's Useful to Split a Vector into Horizontal and Vertical Components

This is the opposite of finding the resultant — you start from the resultant vector and split it into two **components** at right angles to each other. You're basically **working backwards** from the examples on the other page.

Resolving a vector v into horizontal and vertical components

See pages 16 and 17 for more on resolving.

You get the **horizontal** component v_x like this:

$$\cos\theta = v_x / v$$

$$v_x = v\cos\theta$$

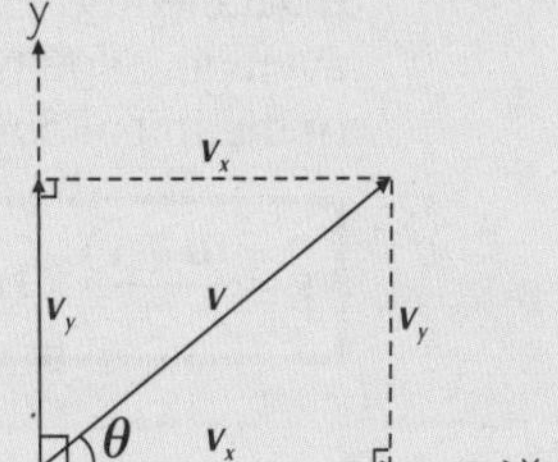

...and the **vertical** component v_y like this:

$$\sin\theta = v_y / v$$

$$v_y = v\sin\theta$$

θ is measured anticlockwise from the horizontal.

Example

Charley's amazing floating home is travelling at a speed of 5 ms^{-1} at an angle of 60° up from the horizontal. Find the vertical and horizontal components.

Charley's mobile home was the envy of all his friends.

The **horizontal** component v_x is:

$v_x = v\cos\theta = \mathbf{5\cos 60°} = 2.5$ ms^{-1}

The vertical component v_y is:

$v_y = v\sin\theta = \mathbf{5\sin 60°} = 4.33$ ms^{-1}

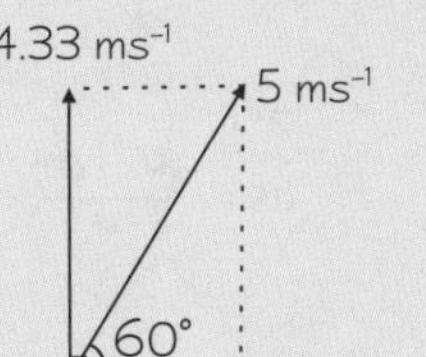

Resolving is dead useful because the two components of a vector **don't affect each other**. This means you can deal with the two directions **completely separately**.

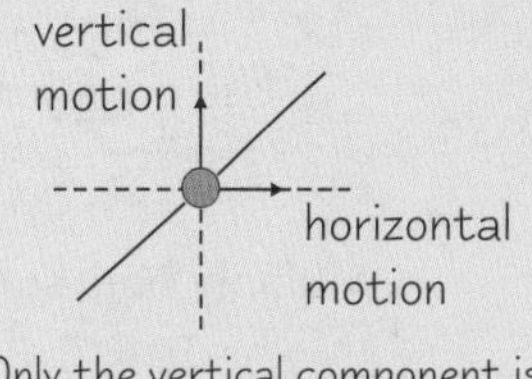

Only the vertical component is affected by gravity.

Practice Questions

Q1 Explain the difference between a scalar quantity and a vector quantity.

Q2 Jemima has gone for a swim in a river which is flowing at 0.35 ms^{-1}. She swims at 0.18 ms^{-1} at right angles to the current. Show that her resultant velocity is 0.39 ms^{-1} at an angle of 27.2° to the current.

Q3 Jemima is pulling on her lead with a force of 40 N at an angle of 26° below the horizontal. Show that the horizontal component of this force is about 36 N.

Exam Questions

Q1 The wind is creating a horizontal force of 20 N on a falling rock of weight 75 N. The angle of the resultant force from the vertical is

A 12.6° **B** 14.9° **C** 16.3° **D** 18.1° [1 mark]

Q2 A glider is travelling at a velocity of 20.0 ms^{-1} at an angle of 15° below the horizontal. Find the horizontal and vertical components of the glider's velocity. [2 marks]

His Dark Vectors Trilogy — displacement, velocity and acceleration...

Well there's nothing like starting the book on a high. And this is nothing like... yes, OK. Ahem. Well, good evening folks. I'll mostly be handing out useful information in boxes like this. But I thought I'd not rush into it, so this one's totally useless.

Motion with Constant Acceleration

Uniform means constant here. It's nothing to do with what you wear.

Uniform Acceleration is Constant Acceleration

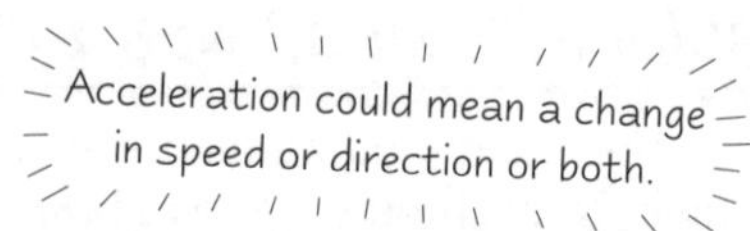

There are **four main equations** that you use to solve problems involving **uniform acceleration** — and you need to be able to use them.

1) **Acceleration is the rate of change of velocity.**
From this definition you get:

$$a = \frac{(v - u)}{t} \quad \text{so} \quad v = u + at$$

where:

u = initial velocity
v = final velocity
a = acceleration
t = time taken

2) **s = average velocity × time**
If acceleration is constant, the average velocity is just the average of the initial and final velocities, so:

$$s = \frac{(u + v)}{2} \times t$$

s = displacement

3) Substitute the expression for v from equation 1 into equation 2 to give:

$$s = \frac{(u + u + at) \times t}{2} = \frac{2ut + at^2}{2}$$

$$s = ut + \tfrac{1}{2}at^2$$

4) The fourth equation comes from equations **1** and **2**:

Use equation **1** in the form: $a = \frac{v - u}{t}$

Multiply both sides by s, where: $s = \frac{(u + v)}{2} \times t$

This gives us: $as = \frac{(v - u)}{t} \times \frac{(u + v)t}{2}$

The t's on the right cancel, so:

$2as = (v - u)(v + u)$

$2as = v^2 - uv + uv - u^2$

so: $v^2 = u^2 + 2as$

Example

A tile falls from a roof 25 m high. Calculate its speed when it hits the ground and how long it takes to fall. Take $g = 9.8\ ms^{-2}$.

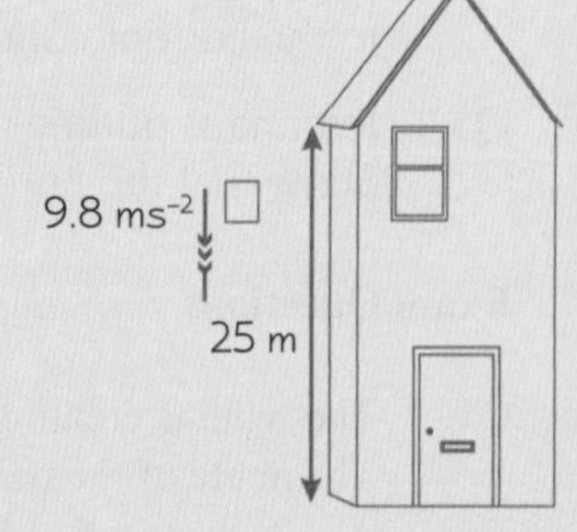

First of all, write out what you know:
$s = 25$ m
$u = 0\ ms^{-1}$ since the tile's stationary to start with
$a = 9.8\ ms^{-2}$ due to gravity
$v = ?$ $t = ?$

Usually you take upwards as the positive direction. In this question it's probably easier to take downwards as positive, so you get $g = +9.8\ ms^{-2}$ instead of $g = -9.8\ ms^{-2}$.

Then, choose an equation with only **one unknown quantity**.
So start with $v^2 = u^2 + 2as$
$v^2 = 0 + 2 \times 9.8 \times 25$
$v^2 = 490$
$v = 22.1\ ms^{-1}$

Now, find t using:
$s = ut + \tfrac{1}{2}at^2$
$25 = 0 + \tfrac{1}{2} \times 9.8 \times t^2$
$t^2 = \frac{25}{4.9}$

Final answers:
$t = 2.3$ s
$v = 22.1\ ms^{-1}$

Motion with Constant Acceleration

Example

A car accelerates steadily from rest at a rate of 4.2 ms^{-2} for 6 seconds.

a) Calculate the final speed.

b) Calculate the distance travelled in 6 seconds.

Remember — always start by writing down what you know.

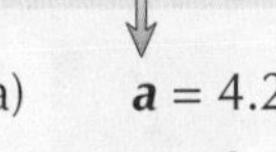

a) $a = 4.2$ ms^{-2} choose the right equation... $v = u + at$

$u = 0$ ms^{-1} $v = 0 + 4.2 \times 6$

$t = 6$ s ***Final answer:*** $v = 25.2$ ms^{-1}

$v = ?$

b) $s = ?$

$t = 6$ s

$u = 0$ ms^{-1}

$a = 4.2$ ms^{-2}

$v = 25.2$ ms^{-1}

you can use: $s = \frac{(u+v)t}{2}$ ⇓ $s = \frac{(0+25.2)\times 6}{2}$ ⇓ ***Final answer:*** $s = 75.6$ m

or: $s = ut + \frac{1}{2}at^2$ ⇓ $s = 0 + \frac{1}{2} \times 4.2 \times (6)^2$ ⇓ $s = 75.6$ m

You Have to **Learn** the Constant Acceleration **Equations**

Make sure you learn the equations. There are only four of them and these questions are always dead easy marks in the exam, so you'd be dafter than a hedgehog in a helicopter not to learn them...

Practice Questions

Q1 Write out the four constant acceleration equations.

Exam Questions

Q1 A skydiver jumps from an aeroplane when it is flying horizontally. She accelerates due to gravity for 5 s.
(a) Calculate her maximum vertical velocity. (Assume no air resistance.) [2 marks]
(b) How far does she fall in this time? [2 marks]

Q2 A motorcyclist slows down uniformly as he approaches a red light. He takes 3.2 seconds to come to a halt and travels 40 m in this time.
(a) How fast was he travelling initially? [2 marks]
(b) Calculate his acceleration. (N.B. a negative value shows a deceleration.) [2 marks]

Q3 A stream provides a constant acceleration of 6 ms^{-2}. A toy boat is pushed directly against the current and then released from a point 1.2 m upstream from a small waterfall. Just before it reaches the waterfall, it is travelling at a speed of 5 ms^{-1}.
(a) Find the initial velocity of the boat. [2 marks]
(b) What is the maximum distance upstream from the waterfall the boat reaches? [2 marks]

Constant acceleration — it'll end in tears...

If a question talks about "uniform" or "constant" acceleration, it's a dead giveaway they want you to use one of these equations. The tricky bit is working out which one to use — start every question by writing out what you know and what you need to know. That makes it much easier to see which equation you need. To be sure. Arrr.

Free Fall and Projectile Motion

Here's a double page spread on how to calculate the air speed velocity of an unladen swallow. And stuff.

Galileo Thought All Objects in **Free Fall** had the **Same Acceleration**

1) **Aristotle** (an ancient Greek philosopher) reckoned that if **two objects** of **different mass** were dropped from the **same height**, the **heavier** object would always hit the ground **first**.
2) **Galileo** disagreed. He thought that **all objects should accelerate towards the ground at the same rate** — so objects with different weights dropped from the same height should hit the ground at the **same time**. Not only that, but he reckoned the reason objects **didn't** do this was because of the effect of **air resistance** on different objects.
3) Galileo's theories eventually overturned Aristotle's and became **generally accepted**. He wasn't the first person to question Aristotle, but his success was down to the **systematic** and **rigorous experiments** he used to **test** his theories. These experiments could be repeated and the results described **mathematically** and compared.

Another gravity experiment.

Free Fall is when there's Only **Gravity** and Nothing Else

Free fall is defined as "the motion of an object undergoing an acceleration of 'g'". You need to remember:

1) Acceleration is a **vector quantity** — and 'g' acts **vertically downwards**.
2) Unless you're given a different value, take the magnitude of g as **9.81 ms^{-2}**, though it varies slightly at different points on the Earth's surface.
3) The **only force** acting on an object in free fall is its **weight**.
4) Objects can have an initial velocity in any direction and still undergo **free fall** as long as the **force** providing the initial velocity is **no longer acting**.

You can Just **Replace a** with **g** in the **Equations of Motion**

You need to be able to work out **speeds**, **distances** and **times** for objects in **free fall**. Since g is a **constant acceleration** you can use the **constant acceleration equations**. But g acts downwards, so you need to be careful about directions.

To make it clear, there's a sign convention: **upwards is positive**, **downwards is negative**.

Sign Conventions — Learn Them:

g is always downwards so it's usually negative	t is always positive
u and v can be either positive or negative	s can be either positive or negative

Case 1: No initial velocity (it just falls)

Initial velocity $u = 0$

Acceleration $a = g = -9.81$ ms^{-2}

So the constant acceleration equations become:

$$v = gt \qquad v^2 = 2gs$$
$$s = \frac{1}{2}gt^2 \qquad s = \frac{vt}{2}$$

Case 2: An initial velocity upwards (it's thrown up into the air)

The constant acceleration equations are just as normal, but with $a = g = -9.81$ ms^{-2}

Case 3: An initial velocity downwards (it's thrown down)

Example: Alex throws a stone down a cliff. She gives it a downwards velocity of 2 ms^{-1}. It takes 3 s to reach the water below. How high is the cliff?

1) You know $u = -2$ ms^{-1}, $a = g = -9.81$ ms^{-2} and $t = 3$ s. You need to find s.

s will be negative because the stone ends up further down than it started

2) Use $s = ut + \frac{1}{2}gt^2 = (-2\times3) + \left(\frac{1}{2}\times-9.81\times3^2\right) = -50.1$ m. **The cliff is 50.1 m high.**

Free Fall and Projectile Motion

Any object given an initial velocity and then left to move freely under gravity is a projectile.
If you're doing AS Maths, you've got all this to look forward to in M1 as well, quite likely. Fun for all the family.

You have to think of **Horizontal** and **Vertical** Motion **Separately**

Example

Sharon fires a scale model of a TV talent show presenter horizontally with a velocity of 100 ms^{-1} from 1.5 m above the ground. How long does it take to hit the ground, and how far does it travel? Assume the model acts as a particle, the ground is horizontal and there is no air resistance.

Think about vertical motion first:

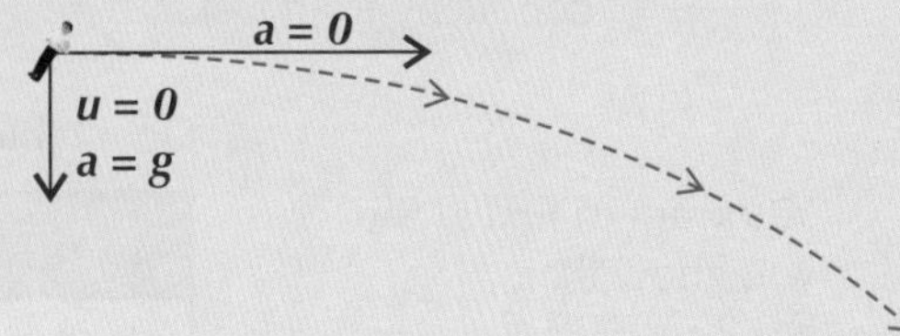

1) It's **constant acceleration** under gravity...
2) You know $\boldsymbol{u} = 0$ (no vertical velocity at first), $\boldsymbol{s} = -1.5$ m and $\boldsymbol{a} = \mathbf{g} = -9.81$ ms^{-2}. You need to find $\boldsymbol{t}$.
3) Use 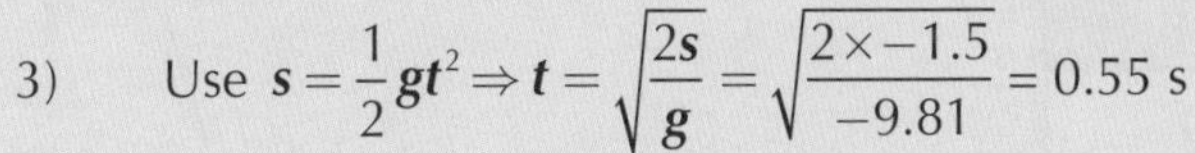 $s = \frac{1}{2}gt^2 \Rightarrow t = \sqrt{\frac{2s}{g}} = \sqrt{\frac{2 \times -1.5}{-9.81}} = 0.55$ s
4) So the model hits the ground after **0.55** seconds.

Then do the horizontal motion:

1) The horizontal motion isn't affected by gravity or any other force, so it moves at a **constant speed**.
2) That means you can just use good old **speed = distance / time**.
3) Now $v_h = 100$ ms^{-1}, $t = 0.55$ s and $a = 0$. You need to find s_h.
4) $s_h = v_h t = 100 \times 0.55 =$ **55 m**

Where v_h is the horizontal velocity, and s_h is the horizontal distance travelled (rather than the height fallen).

It's **Slightly Trickier** if it **Starts Off** at an **Angle**

If something's projected at an angle (like, say, a javelin) you start off with both horizontal and vertical velocity:

Method:
1) Resolve the initial velocity into horizontal and vertical components.
2) Use the vertical component to work out how long it's in the air and/or how high it goes.
3) Use the horizontal component to work out how far it goes while it's in the air.

Practice Questions

Q1 What is the initial vertical velocity for an object projected horizontally with a velocity of 5 ms^{-1}?

Q2 How does the horizontal velocity of a free-falling object change with time?

Exam Questions

Q1 Jason stands on a vertical cliff edge throwing stones into the sea below.
He throws a stone horizontally with a velocity of 20 ms^{-1}, 560 m above sea level.
(a) How long does it take for the stone to hit the water from leaving Jason's hand?
Use g = 9.81 ms^{-2} and ignore air resistance. [2 marks]
(b) Find the distance of the stone from the base of the cliff when it hits the water. [2 marks]

Q2 Robin fires an arrow into the air with a vertical velocity of 30 ms^{-1}, and a horizontal velocity of 20 ms^{-1}, from 1 m above the ground. Find the maximum height from the ground reached by his arrow.
Use g = 9.81 ms^{-2} and ignore air resistance. [3 marks]

Is that an African swallow or a European swallow...

Ah, the ups and downs and er... acrosses of life. Make sure you're happy splitting an object's motion into horizontal and vertical bits — it comes up all over mechanics. Hmmm... I wonder what Galileo would be proudest of — insisting on the systematic, rigorous experimental method on which modern science hangs... or getting in a Queen song? Magnificoooooo...

Displacement-Time Graphs

Drawing graphs by hand — oh joy. You'd think examiners had never heard of the graphical calculator. Ah well, until they manage to drag themselves out of the dark ages, you'll just have to grit your teeth and get on with it.

Acceleration *Means a* ***Curved Displacement-Time Graph***

A graph of displacement against time for an **accelerating object** always produces a **curve**.
If the object is accelerating at a **uniform rate**, then the **rate of change** of the **gradient** will be constant.

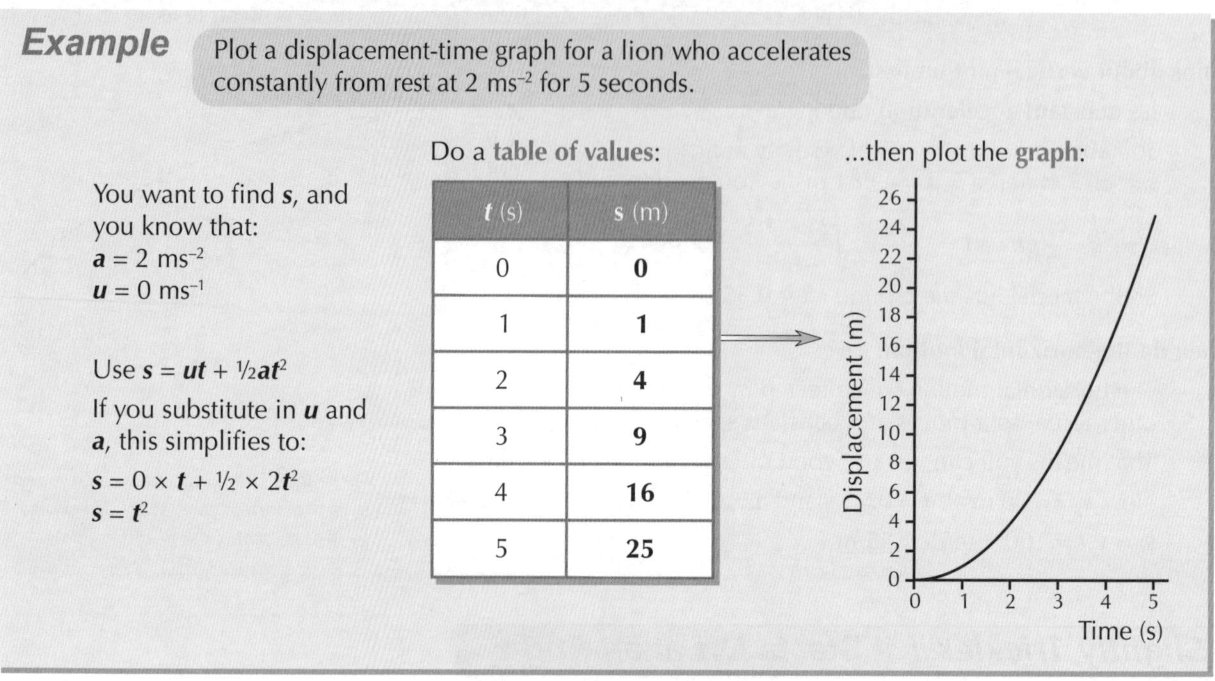

Example Plot a displacement-time graph for a lion who accelerates constantly from rest at 2 ms^{-2} for 5 seconds.

You want to find **s**, and you know that:
$\mathbf{a} = 2$ ms^{-2}
$\mathbf{u} = 0$ ms^{-1}

Use $\mathbf{s} = \mathbf{ut} + \frac{1}{2}\mathbf{at}^2$
If you substitute in ***u*** and ***a***, this simplifies to:
$\mathbf{s} = 0 \times \mathbf{t} + \frac{1}{2} \times 2\mathbf{t}^2$
$\mathbf{s} = \mathbf{t}^2$

Do a **table of values:**

t (s)	s (m)
0	**0**
1	**1**
2	**4**
3	**9**
4	**16**
5	**25**

...then plot the **graph**:

Different Accelerations Have ***Different Gradients***

In the example above, if the lion has a **different acceleration** it'll change the **gradient** of the curve like this:

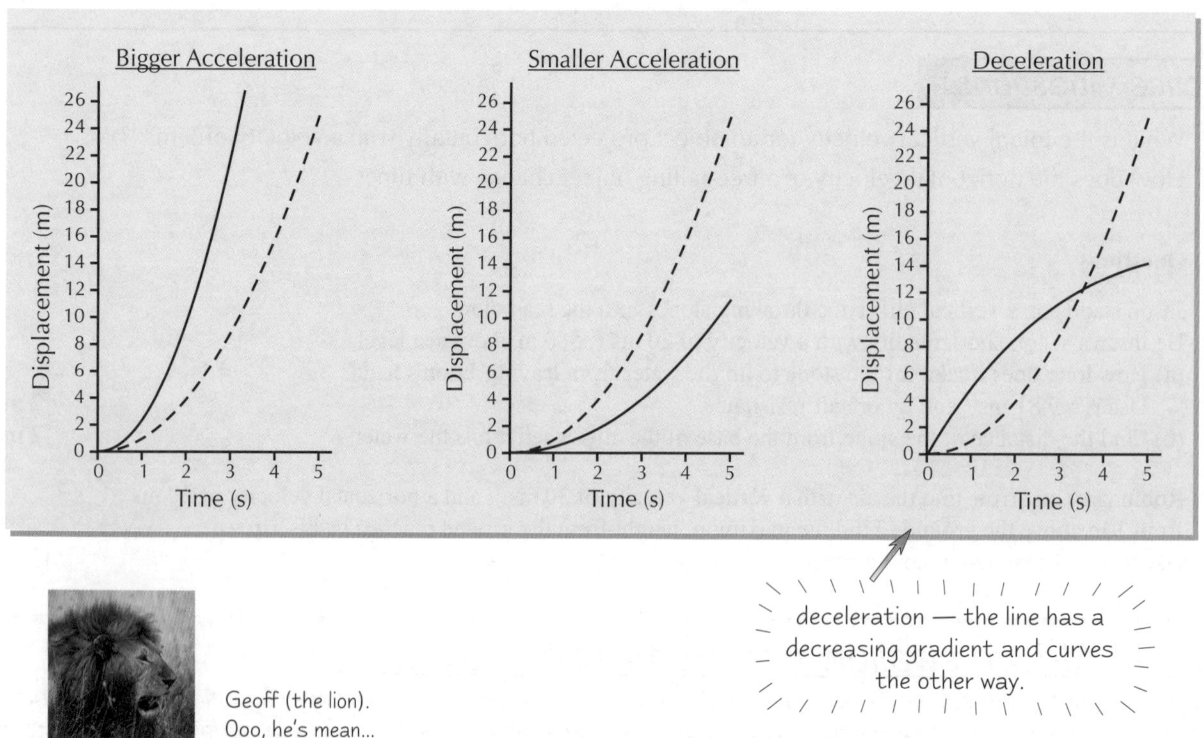

Geoff (the lion).
Ooo, he's mean...

Displacement-Time Graphs

The **Gradient** of a **Displacement-Time Graph** Tells You the Velocity

When the velocity is constant, the graph's a **straight line**. Velocity is defined as...

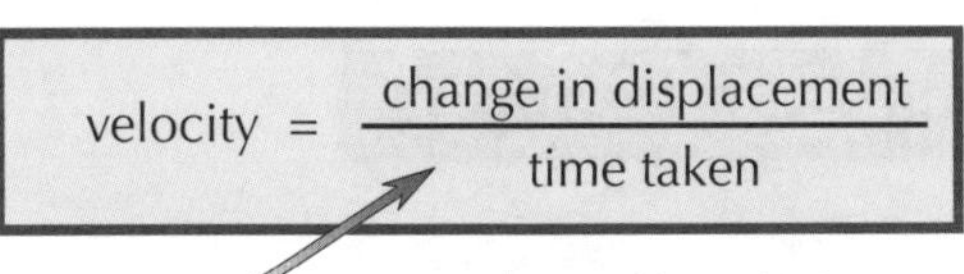

$$\text{velocity} = \frac{\text{change in displacement}}{\text{time taken}}$$

On the graph, this is $\frac{\text{change in } y\ (\Delta y)}{\text{change in } x\ (\Delta x)}$, i.e. the gradient.

So to get the velocity from a displacement-time graph, just find the gradient.

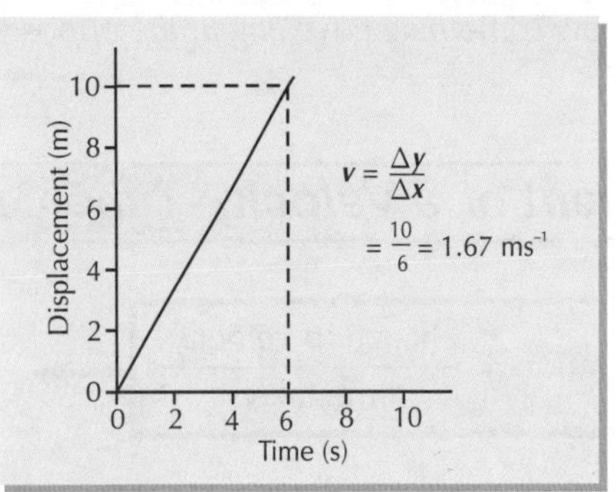

It's the Same with **Curved Graphs**

If the gradient **isn't constant** (i.e. if it's a curved line), it means the object is **accelerating**.

To find the **velocity** at a certain point you need to draw a **tangent** to the curve at that point and find its gradient.

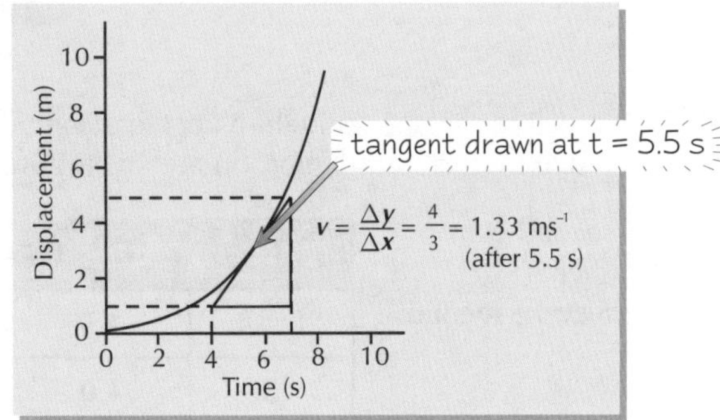

Practice Questions

Q1 What is given by the slope of a displacement-time graph?

Q2 Sketch a displacement-time graph to show: a) constant velocity, b) acceleration, c) deceleration

Exam Questions

Q1 Describe the motion of the cyclist as shown by the graph below. [4 marks]

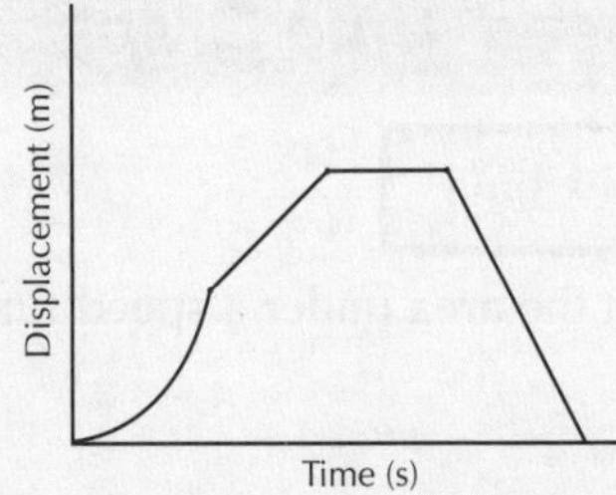

Q2 A baby crawls 5 m in 8 seconds at a constant velocity. She then rests for 5 seconds before crawling a further 3 m in 5 seconds. Finally, she makes her way back to her starting point in 10 seconds, travelling at a constant speed all the way.
(a) Draw a displacement-time graph to show the baby's journey. [4 marks]
(b) Calculate her velocity at all the different stages of her journey. [2 marks]

Some curves are bigger than others...

Whether it's a straight line or a curve, the steeper it is, the greater the velocity. There's nothing difficult about these graphs — the main problem is that it's easy to get them muddled up with velocity-time graphs (next page). If in doubt, think about the gradient — is it velocity or acceleration, is it changing (curve), is it constant (straight line), is it 0 (horizontal line)...

Velocity-Time Graphs

Speed-time graphs and velocity-time graphs are pretty similar. The big difference is that velocity-time graphs can have a negative part to show something travelling in the opposite direction:

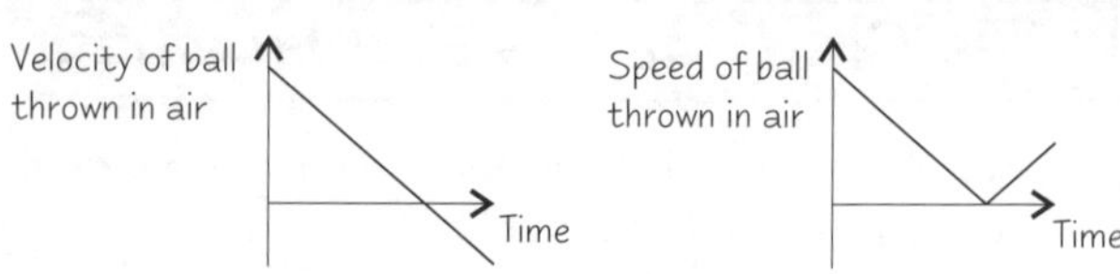

*The **Gradient** of a **Velocity-Time Graph** tells you the **Acceleration***

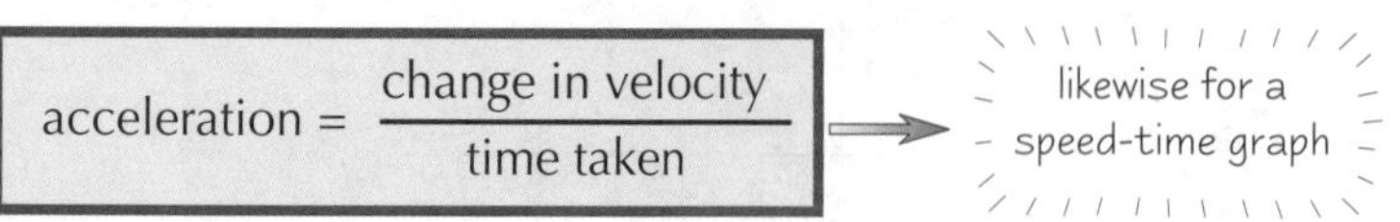

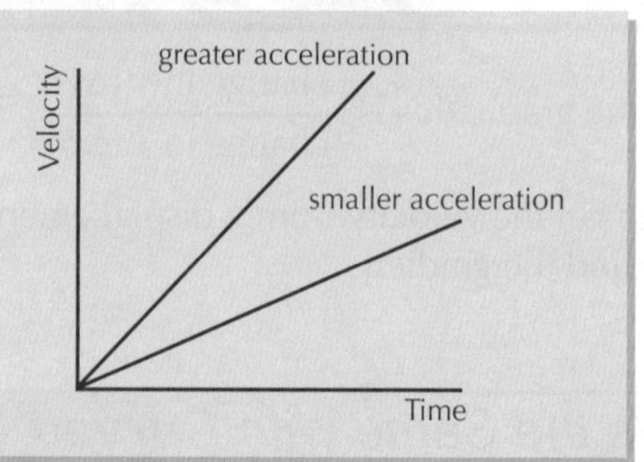

So the acceleration is just the **gradient** of a **velocity-time graph**.

1) **Uniform** acceleration is always a **straight line**.
2) The **steeper** the **gradient**, the **greater** the **acceleration**.

Example

A lion strolls along at 1.5 ms^{-1} for 4 s and then accelerates uniformly at a rate of 2.5 ms^{-2} for 4 s. Plot this information on a velocity-time graph.

Gordon (the lion)...

So, for the first four seconds, the velocity is 1.5 ms^{-1}, then it increases by **2.5 ms^{-1} every second**:

t (s)	v (ms^{-1})
0 – 4	**1.5**
5	**4.0**
6	**6.5**
7	**9.0**
8	**11.5**

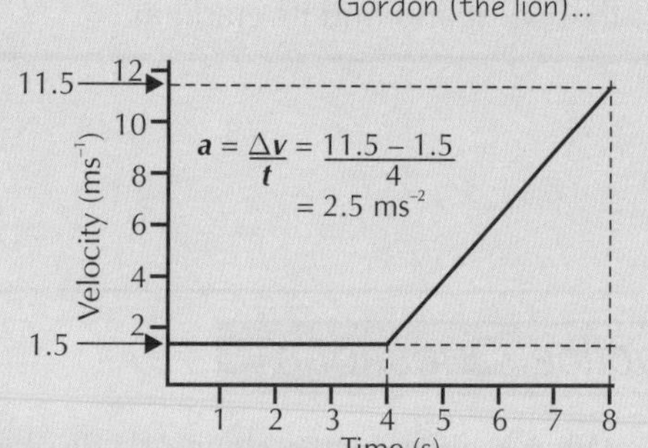

You can see that the **gradient of the line** is **constant** between 4 s and 8 s and has a value of 2.5 ms^{-2}, representing the **acceleration of the lion.**

Distance** Travelled = **Area** under **Speed-Time Graph

You know that:

distance travelled = average speed × time

So you can find the distance travelled by working out the **area under a speed-time graph**.

Example

A racing car accelerates uniformly from rest to 40 ms^{-1} in 10 s. It maintains this speed for a further 20 s before coming to rest by decelerating at a constant rate over the next 15 s. Draw a velocity-time graph for this journey and use it to calculate the total distance travelled by the racing car.

Split the **graph** up into **sections**: A, B and C

Calculate the **area** of each and **add** the three results together.

A: Area = ½ base × height = ½ × 10 × 40 = 200 m

B: Area = b × h = 20 × 40 = 800 m

C: Area = ½ b × h = ½ × 15 × 40 = 300 m

Total distance travelled = 1300 m

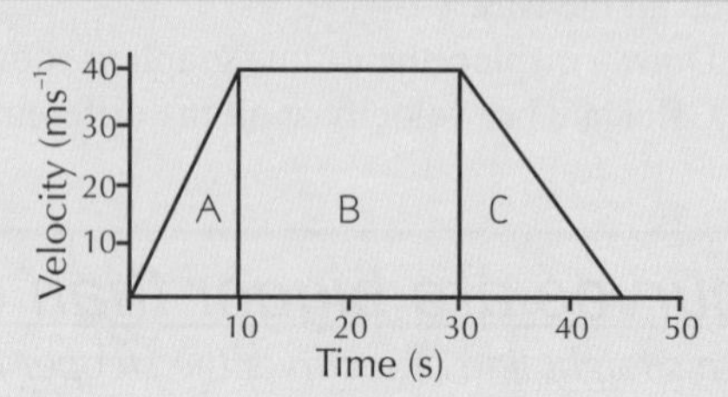

Velocity-Time Graphs

Non-Uniform Acceleration is a Curve on a V-T Graph

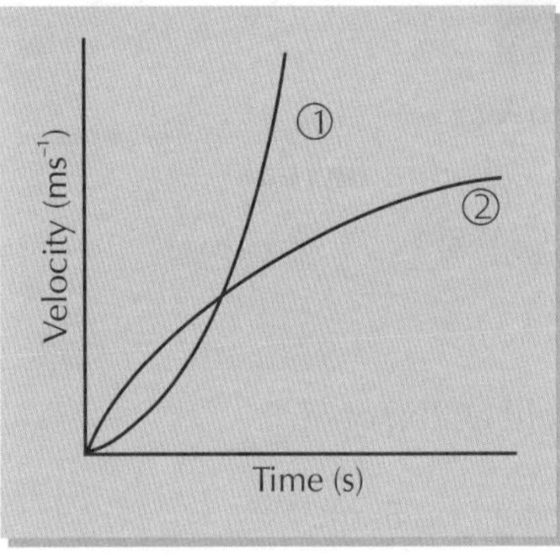

1) If the acceleration is changing, the gradient of the velocity-time graph will also be changing — so you **won't** get a **straight line**.
2) **Increasing acceleration** is shown by an **increasing gradient** — like in curve ①.
3) **Decreasing acceleration** is shown by a **decreasing gradient** — like in curve ②.

Simple enough...

You Can Draw Displacement-Time and Velocity-Time Graphs Using ICT

Instead of gathering distance and time data using **traditional methods**, e.g. a stopwatch and ruler, you can be a bit more **high-tech**.

A fairly **standard** piece of kit you can use for motion experiments is an **ultrasound position detector**. This is a type of **data-logger** that automatically records the **distance** of an object from the sensor several times a second.

If you attach one of these detectors to a computer with **graph-drawing software**, you can get **real-time** displacement-time and velocity-time graphs.

The main **advantages** of data-loggers over traditional methods are:

1) The data is more **accurate** — you don't have to allow for human reaction times.
2) Automatic systems have a much higher **sampling** rate than humans — most ultrasound position detectors can take a reading ten times every second.
3) You can see the data displayed in **real time**.

Practice Questions

Q1 How do you calculate acceleration from a velocity-time graph?

Q2 How do you calculate the distance travelled from a speed-time graph?

Q3 Sketch velocity-time graphs for constant velocity and constant acceleration.

Q4 Describe the main advantages of ICT over traditional methods for the collection and display of motion data.

Exam Question

Q1 A skier accelerates uniformly from rest at 2 ms^{-2} down a straight slope.

(a) Sketch a velocity-time graph for the first 5 s of his journey. [2 marks]

(b) Use a constant acceleration equation to calculate his displacement at t = 1, 2, 3, 4 and 5 s, and plot this information onto a displacement-time graph. [5 marks]

(c) Suggest another method of calculating the skier's distance travelled after each second and use this to check your answers to part (b). [2 marks]

Still awake — I'll give you five more minutes...

There's a really nice sunset outside my window. It's one of those ones that makes the whole landscape go pinky-yellowish. And that's about as much interest as I can muster on this topic. Normal service will be resumed on page 14, I hope.

Mass, Weight and Centre of Gravity

I'm sure you know all this 'mass', 'weight' and 'density' stuff from GCSE. But let's just make sure...

The Mass of a Body makes it Resist Changes in Motion

1) The **mass** of an object is the **amount of 'stuff'** (or **matter**) in it. It's measured in **kg**.
2) The greater an object's mass, the greater its **resistance** to a **change in velocity** (called its **inertia**).
3) The **mass** of an object **doesn't change** if the strength of the **gravitational field** changes.
4) Weight is a **force**. It's measured in **newtons** (N), like all forces.
5) Weight is the **force experienced by a mass** due to a **gravitational field**.
6) The weight of an object **does vary** according to the size of the **gravitational field** acting on it.

weight = mass × gravitational field strength ($W = mg$) where $g = 9.81\ \text{Nkg}^{-1}$ on Earth.

This table shows Bernard (the lion*)'s mass and weight on the Earth and the Moon.

Name	Quantity	Earth ($g = 9.81\ \text{Nkg}^{-1}$)	Moon ($g = 1.6\ \text{Nkg}^{-1}$)
Mass	Mass (scalar)	150 kg	150 kg
Weight	Force (vector)	1471.5 N	240 N

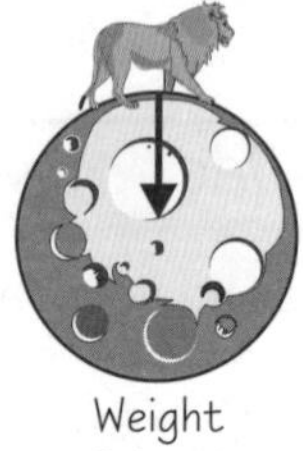

Weight
1470 N

Density is Mass per Unit Volume

Density is a measure of the 'compactness' (for want of a better word) of a substance.
It relates the mass of a substance to how much space it takes up.

$$\text{density} = \frac{\text{mass}}{\text{volume}} \qquad \rho = \frac{m}{V}$$

The symbol for density is a Greek letter rho (ρ) — it looks like a p but it isn't.

The **units** of **density** are **$g\,cm^{-3}$** or **$kg\,m^{-3}$**
N.B. $1\ g\,cm^{-3} = 1000\ kg\,m^{-3}$

1) The density of an object depends on what it's made of. Density **doesn't vary** with **size or shape**.
2) The **average density** of an object determines whether it **floats** or **sinks**.
3) A solid object will **float** on a fluid if it has a **lower density** than the **fluid**.

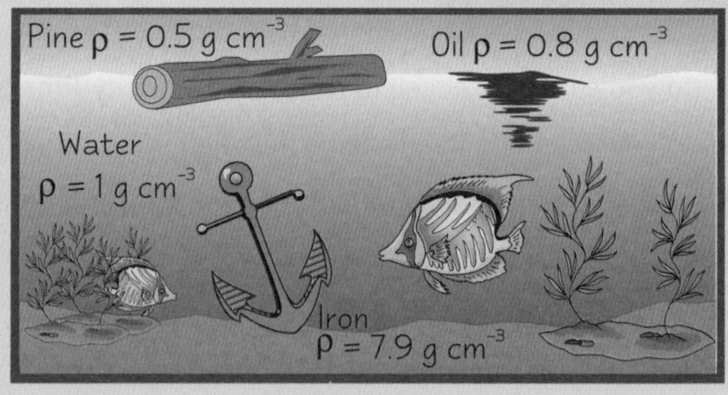

Centre of Gravity — Assume All the Mass is in One Place

1) The **centre of gravity** (or centre of mass) of an object is the **single point** that you can consider its **whole weight** to **act through** (whatever its orientation).
2) The object will always **balance** around this **point**, although in some cases the **centre of gravity** will **fall outside** the object.

*Yes, I know — I just like lions, OK.

Mass, Weight and Centre of Gravity

Find the *Centre of Gravity* either by *Symmetry* or *Experiment*

Experiment to find the Centre of Gravity of an Irregular Object

1) Hang the object freely from a point (e.g. one corner).
2) Draw a vertical line downwards from the point of suspension — use a plumb bob to get your line exactly vertical.
3) Hang the object from a different point.
4) Draw another vertical line down.
5) The centre of gravity is where the two lines cross.

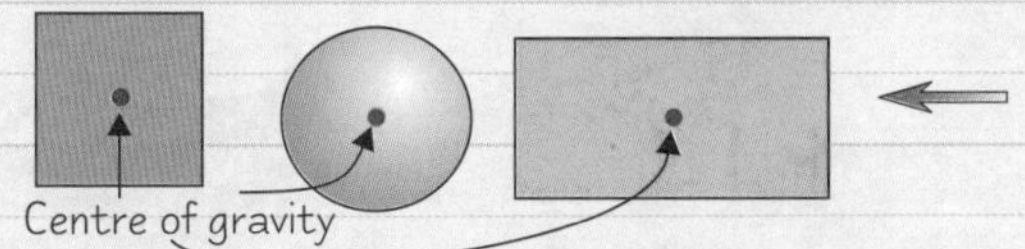

For a regular object you can just use symmetry. The centre of gravity of any regular shape is at its centre.

How High the *Centre of Gravity* is tells you *How Stable* the Object is

1) An object will be nice and **stable** if it has a **low centre** of **gravity** and a **wide base area**. This idea is used a lot in design, e.g. Formula 1 racing cars.

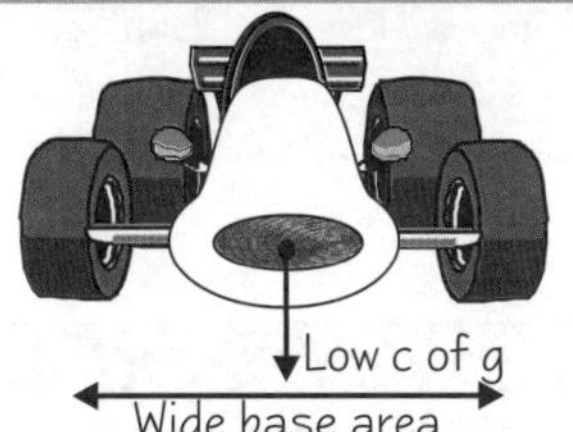

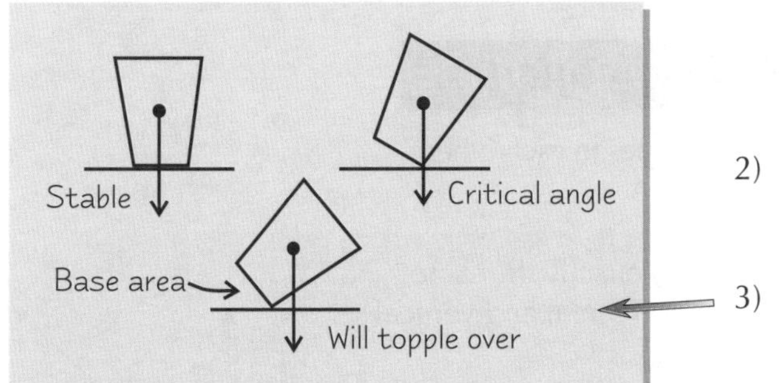

2) The **higher** the **centre of gravity**, and the **smaller** the **base area**, the **less stable** the object will be. Think of unicyclists...
3) An object will topple over if a **vertical line** drawn **downwards** from its **centre of gravity** falls **outside** its **base area**.

Practice Questions

Q1 A lioness has a mass of 200 kg. What would be her mass and weight on the Earth (where $g = 9.8\ \text{Nkg}^{-1}$) and on the Moon (where $g = 1.6\ \text{Nkg}^{-1}$)?

Q2 What is meant by the centre of gravity of an object?

Exam Questions

Q1 (a) Define **density**. [1 mark]

(b) A cylinder of aluminium, radius 4 cm and height 6 cm, has a mass of 820 g. Calculate its density. [3 marks]

(c) Use the information from part (b) to calculate the mass of a cube of aluminium of side 5 cm. [1 mark]

Q2 Describe an experiment to find the centre of gravity of an object of uniform density with a constant thickness and irregular cross-section. Identify one major source of uncertainty and suggest a way to reduce its effect on the accuracy of your result. [5 marks]

The centre of gravity of this book should be round about page 48...

This is a really useful area of physics. To would-be nuclear physicists it might seem a little dull, but if you want to be an engineer — something a bit more useful (no offence Einstein) — then things like centre of gravity and density are dead important things to understand. You know, for designing things like cars and submarines... yep, pretty useful I'd say.

Forces

Remember the vector stuff from the beginning of the section... good, you're going to need it...

Free-Body Force Diagrams show All Forces on a Single Body

1) **Free-body force** diagrams show a **single body** on its own.
2) The diagram should include all the **forces** that **act on** the body, but **not** the **forces it exerts** on the rest of the world.
3) Remember **forces** are **vector quantities** and so the **arrow labels** should show the **size** and **direction** of the forces.
4) If a body is in **equilibrium** (i.e. not accelerating) the **forces** acting on it will be **balanced**.

Drawing free-body force diagrams isn't too hard — you just need practice. Here are a few **examples**:

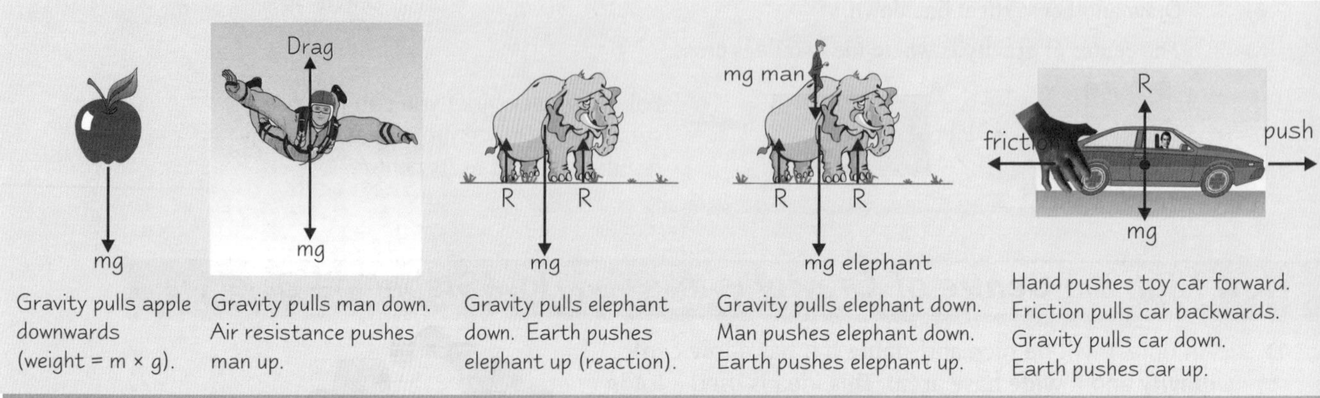

Resolving a Force means Splitting it into Components

1) Forces can be in **any direction**, so they're not always at right angles to each other. This is sometimes a bit **awkward** for **calculations**.
2) To make an 'awkward' force easier to deal with, you can think of it as **two separate forces**, acting at **right angles** to **each other**.

The force ***F*** has exactly the same effect as the horizontal and vertical forces, F_H and F_V.
Replacing ***F*** with F_H and F_V is called **resolving the force *F***.

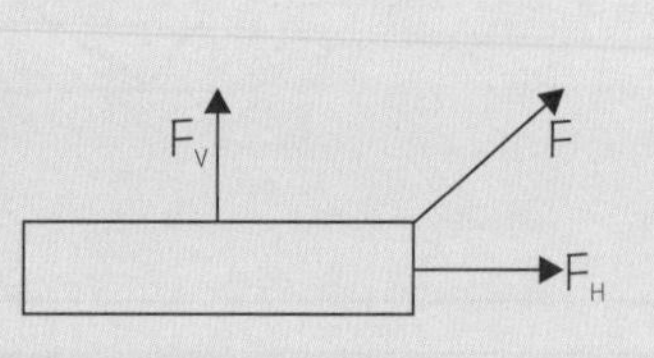

3) To find the size of a component force in a particular direction, you need to use trigonometry (see page 5). Forces are vectors, so you treat them in the same way as velocities — put them end to end.

So this...

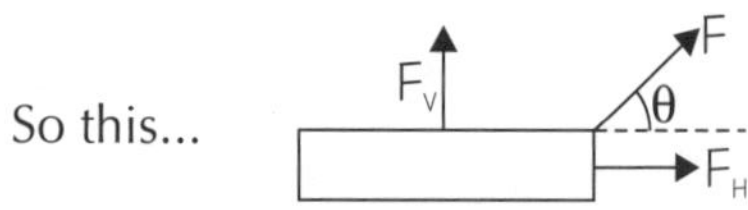

...could be drawn like this:

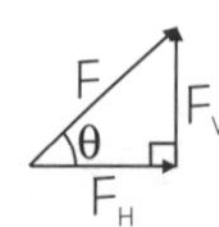

Using trig. you get:

$$\frac{F_H}{F} = \cos\theta \quad \textbf{or} \quad F_H = F\cos\theta$$

And:

$$\frac{F_V}{F} = \sin\theta \quad \textbf{or} \quad F_V = F\sin\theta$$

Example

A tree trunk is pulled along the ground by an elephant exerting a force of 1200 N at an angle of 25° to the horizontal. Calculate the components of this force in the horizontal and vertical directions.

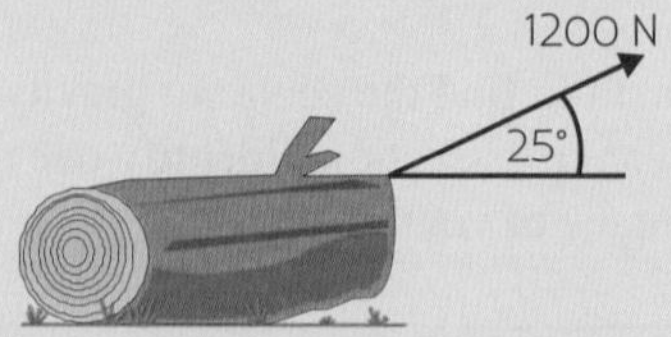

Horizontal force = 1200 × cos 25° = **1088 N**
Vertical force = 1200 × sin 25° = **507 N**

Forces

You Add the Components Back Together to get the Resultant Force

1) If **two forces** act on an object, you find the **resultant** (total) **force** by adding the **vectors** together and creating a **closed triangle**, with the resultant force represented by the **third side**.
2) Forces are vectors (as you know), so you use **vector addition** — draw the forces as vector arrows put 'tail to top'.
3) Then it's yet more trigonometry to find the **angle** and the **length** of the third side.

Example

Two dung beetles roll a dung ball along the ground at constant velocity. Beetle A applies a force of 0.5 N northwards while beetle B exerts a force of only 0.2 N eastwards. What is the resultant force on the dung ball?

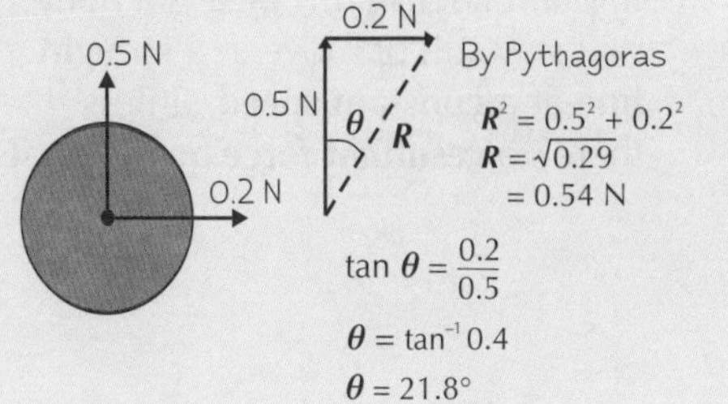

The resultant force is **0.54 N** at an angle of **21.8°** from North.

Choose sensible Axes for Resolving

Use directions that **make sense** for the situation you're dealing with. If you've got an object on a slope, choose your directions **along the slope** and **at right angles to it**. You can turn the paper to an angle if that helps.

Always choose sensible axes

Examiners like to call a slope an "inclined plane".

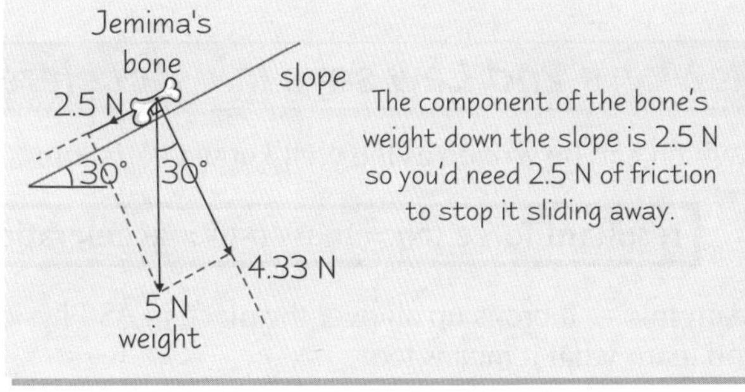

Practice Questions

Q1 Sketch a free-body force diagram for an ice hockey puck moving across the ice (assuming no friction).

Q2 What are the horizontal and vertical components of the force F?

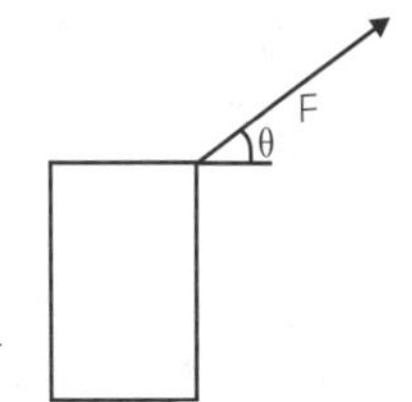

Exam Questions

Q1 A picture is suspended from a hook as shown in the diagram. The tension force, T, in the string is

A 36.9 N **B** 51.2 N

C 78.48 N **D** 102.45 N

[1 mark]

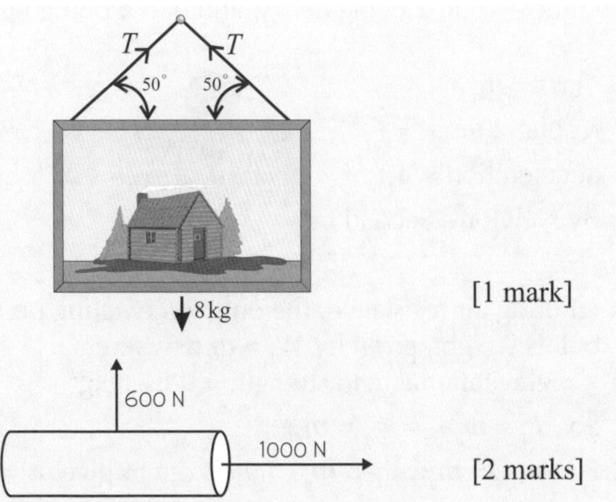

Q2 Two elephants pull a tree trunk as shown in the diagram. Calculate the resultant force on the tree trunk.

[2 marks]

Free-body force diagram — sounds like something you'd get with a dance mat...

*Remember those F cos θ and F sin θ bits. Write them on bits of paper and stick them to your wall. Scrawl them on your pillow. Tattoo them on your brain. Whatever it takes — you just **have to learn them**.*

Newton's Laws of Motion

You did most of this at GCSE, but that doesn't mean you can just skip over it now. You'll be kicking yourself if you forget this stuff in the exam — easy marks...

Newton's **1st Law** says that a **Force** is Needed to Change Velocity

1) **Newton's 1st law of motion** states that the **velocity** of an object will **not change** unless a **resultant force** acts on it.
2) In plain English this means a body will stay still or move in a **straight line** at a **constant speed**, unless there's a **resultant force** acting on it.

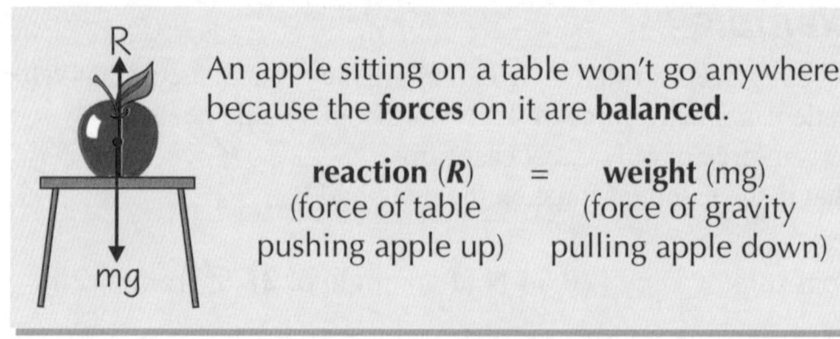

3) If the forces **aren't balanced**, the **overall resultant force** will make the body **accelerate**. This could be a change in **direction**, or **speed**, or both. (See Newton's 2nd law, below.)

Newton's **2nd Law** says that **Acceleration** is **Proportional** to the Force

...which can be written as the well-known equation:

resultant force (N) = mass (kg) × acceleration (ms^{-2})

$$F = m \times a$$

Learn this — it crops up all over the place in AS Physics. And learn what it means too:

1) It says that the **more force** you have acting on a certain mass, the **more acceleration** you get.
2) It says that for a given force the **more mass** you have, the **less acceleration** you get.

REMEMBER:
1) The **resultant force** is the **vector sum** of all the forces.
2) The force is **always** measured in **newtons**.
3) The **mass** is always measured in **kilograms**.
4) The **acceleration** is always in the **same direction** as the **resultant force** and is measured in ms^{-2}.

Galileo said: **All Objects Fall** at the **Same Rate** (if you **Ignore Air Resistance**)

You need to understand **why** this is true. Newton's 2nd law explains it neatly — consider two balls dropped at the same time — ball **1** being heavy, and ball **2** being light. Then use Newton's 2nd law to find their acceleration.

mass = m_1
resultant force = F_1
acceleration = a_1
W_1
By Newton's Second Law:

$$F_1 = m_1 a_1$$

Ignoring air resistance, the only force acting on the ball is weight, given by $W_1 = m_1 g$ (where g = gravitational field strength = 9.81 Nkg^{-1}).
So: $F_1 = m_1 a_1 = W_1 = m_1 g$
So: $m_1 a_1 = m_1 g$, then m_1 cancels out to give: $a_1 = g$

mass = m_2
resultant force = F_2
acceleration = a_2

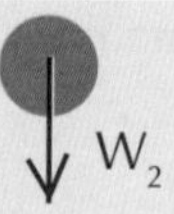

By Newton's Second Law:

$$F_2 = m_2 a_2$$

Ignoring air resistance, the only force acting on the ball is weight, given by $W_2 = m_2 g$ (where g = gravitational field strength = 9.81 Nkg^{-1}).
So: $F_2 = m_2 a_2 = W_2 = m_2 g$
So: $m_2 a_2 = m_2 g$, then m_2 cancels out to give: $a_2 = g$

... in other words, the **acceleration** is **independent of the mass**. It makes **no difference** whether the ball is **heavy or light**. And I've kindly **hammered home the point** by showing you two almost identical examples.

Newton's Laws of Motion

Newton's **3rd Law** says each Force has an **Equal, Opposite Reaction Force**

There are a few different ways of stating Newton's 3rd law, but the clearest way is:

> **If an object A EXERTS a FORCE on object B, then object B exerts AN EQUAL BUT OPPOSITE FORCE on object A.**

You'll also hear the law as "every action has an equal and opposite reaction". But this confuses people who wrongly think the forces are both applied to the same object. (If that were the case, you'd get a resultant force of zero and nothing would ever move anywhere...)

The two forces actually represent the **same interaction**, just seen from two **different perspectives**:

1) If you **push against a wall**, the wall will **push back** against you, **just as hard**. As soon as you stop pushing, so does the wall. Amazing...
2) If you **pull a cart**, whatever force **you exert** on the rope, the rope exerts the **exact opposite** pull on you (unless the rope's stretching).
3) When you go **swimming**, you push **back** against the water with your arms and legs, and the water pushes you **forwards** with an equal-sized force.

This looks like Newton's 3rd law...

But it's NOT.

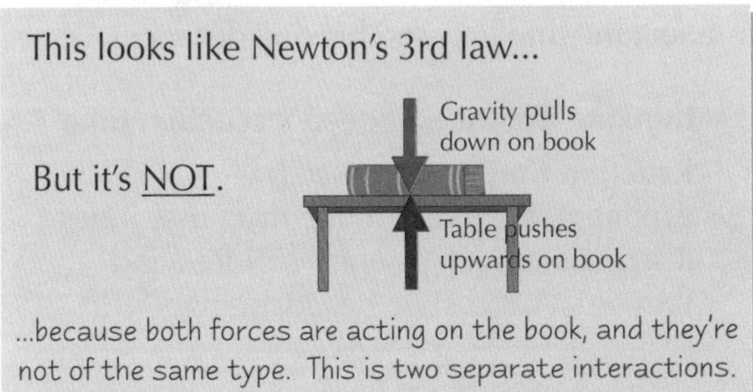

...because both forces are acting on the book, and they're not of the same type. This is two separate interactions. The forces are equal and opposite, resulting in zero acceleration, so this is showing Newton's 1st law.

Newton's 3rd law applies in **all situations** and to all **types of force**. But the pairs of forces are always the **same type**, e.g. both gravitational or both electrical.

Practice Questions

Q1 State Newton's 1st, 2nd and 3rd laws of motion, and explain what they mean.

Q2 What are the two equal and opposite forces acting between an orbiting satellite and the Earth?

Exam Questions

Q1 Draw diagrams to show the forces acting on a parachutist:

(a) accelerating downwards. [1 mark]

(b) having reached terminal velocity. [1 mark]

Q2 A boat is moving across a river. The engines provide a force of 500 N at right angles to the flow of the river and the boat experiences a drag of 100 N in the opposite direction. The force on the boat due to the flow of the river is 300 N. The mass of the boat is 250 kg.

(a) Calculate the magnitude of the resultant force acting on the boat. [2 marks]

(b) Calculate the magnitude of the acceleration of the boat. [2 marks]

Q3 This question asks you to use Newton's second law to explain three situations.

(a) Two cars have different maximum accelerations.
What are the only two overall factors that determine the acceleration a car can have? [2 marks]

(b) Michael can always beat his younger brother Tom in a sprint, however short the distance.
Give two possible reasons for this. [2 marks]

(c) Michael and Tom are both keen on diving. They notice that they seem to take the same time to drop from the diving board to the water. Explain why this is the case. (Assume no air resistance.) [3 marks]

Newton's three incredibly important laws of motion...

These laws may not really fill you with a huge amount of excitement (and I could hardly blame you if they don't)... but it was pretty fantastic at the time — suddenly people actually understood how forces work, and how they affect motion. I mean arguably it was one of the most important scientific discoveries ever...

Mechanics in the Real World

Some real applications now — how to avoid collisions, and how car manufacturers try to make sure you survive.

Many Factors Affect How Quickly a Car Stops

The braking distance and thinking distance together make the **total distance you need to stop** after you see a problem:

Thinking distance + Braking distance = Stopping distance

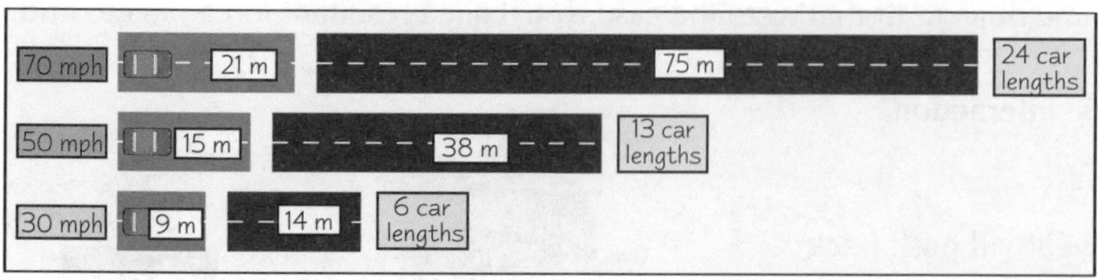

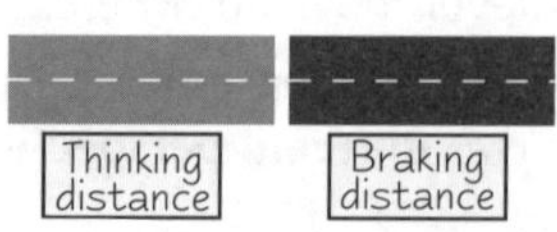

In an exam you might need to list factors that affect the thinking and braking distances.

thinking distance = speed × reaction time

Reaction time is increased by **tiredness**, **alcohol** or other **drug** use, **illness**, **distractions** such as noisy children and Wayne's World-style headbanging.

Braking distance depends on the **braking force**, **friction** between the tyres and the road, the **mass** and the **speed**.

Braking force is reduced by **reduced friction** between the brakes and the wheels (**worn** or **badly adjusted brakes**).

Friction between the tyres and the road is reduced by **wet** or **icy** roads, **leaves or dirt** on the road, **worn-out tyre treads**, etc.

Mass is affected by the size of the car and what you put in it.

Car Safety Features are Usually Designed to Slow You Down Gradually

Modern cars have **safety features** built in. Many of them make use of the idea of slowing the collision down so it **takes you longer to stop**, so your **deceleration is less** and there is **less force** on you.

Safety features you need to know about are:

1) **Seatbelts** keep you in your seat and also 'give' a little so that you're brought to a stop over a longer time.
2) **Airbags** inflate when you have a collision and are big and squishy so they stop you hitting hard things and slow you down gradually. (More about airbags and how they work on the next page.)
3) **Crumple zones** at the front and back of the car are designed to give way more easily and absorb some of the energy of the collision.
4) **Safety cages** are designed to prevent the area around the occupants of the car from being crushed in.

Example

Giles's car bumps into the back of a stationary bus. The car was travelling at 2 ms^{-1} and comes to a stop in 0.2 s. Giles was wearing his seatbelt and takes 0.8 s to stop. The mass of the car is 1000 kg and Giles's mass is 75 kg.

a) Find the decelerations of Giles and the car.

b) Calculate the average force acting on Giles during the accident.

c) Work out the average force that would have acted on Giles if he had stopped in as short a time as the car.

a) Use $\boldsymbol{v} = \boldsymbol{u} + \boldsymbol{at}$:
For the car: $u = 2$ ms^{-1}, $v = 0$, $t = 0.2$ s
Which gives: $0 = 2 + 0.2a \Rightarrow 0.2a = -2 \Rightarrow a = -10$ ms^{-2} so the **deceleration = 10 ms^{-2}**
For Giles: $u = 2$ ms^{-1}, $v = 0$, $t = 0.8$ s
Which gives: $0 = 2 + 0.8a \Rightarrow 0.8a = -2 \Rightarrow a = -2.5$ ms^{-2} so the **deceleration = 2.5 ms^{-2}**

b) Use $F = ma = 75 \times 2.5 =$ **187.5 N**

c) Use $F = ma$ again, but with 10 ms^{-2} instead of 2.5 ms^{-2}: $F = ma = 75 \times 10 =$ **750 N**

Mechanics in the Real World

When you do sport, you probably don't think about the Physics behind it at all. But it is important — e.g. rock climbers have to know that the tension in their ropes will be enough to balance their weight, while the laws of projectile motion govern where a tennis ball or javelin will end up.

Forces Act on Sports People

Whatever you do and wherever you go, there'll **always** be **forces** acting on you. Understanding the **forces** that act on an object allows you to understand how and why it is **moving** (or not moving). For example, the **rock climber** on the right is **not moving** — the forces acting on him are **balanced** (he's in **equilibrium**).

The **bungee jumper** on the left is **accelerating downwards**. Why — because his **weight** is **greater** than the **tension** in the bungee cord (and air resistance). But soon, the tension will **equal the force** of his weight and he'll **stop accelerating** downwards.

In the exam, you could be asked to **draw** a **force diagram**. Remember, if the body is **stationary** or **moving** at a **constant speed**, the forces must be **balanced** — and if it's **accelerating**, there must be a **resultant force** in the direction of the acceleration.

Gravity is the Only Force Acting on Projectiles

All sorts of **sports** — from **ice dancing** to **football** and **athletics** — involve **projectile motion**. The **projectile** could be a **person** (e.g. a long jumper), a **ball** that's been thrown, kicked or hit, or even a **javelin** — the **same rules** apply. There was a full **explanation** and **examples** on **pages 8 and 9**, so go back and **reread** them if you can't remember it.

The most important thing to remember is that once the **object** is in the **air**, the **only** force acting on it is due to **gravity** (and air resistance, but you can normally ignore that).

Practice Questions

Q1 What equation can you use to work out the force you experience during a collision?

Q2 What factor affects both thinking distance and braking distance?

Q3 What is the resultant force on the rock climber in the picture above? How do you know this?

Q4 Name three projectiles used in sports. What force acts on them while they are in the air?

Exam Questions

Q1 Sarah sees a cow step into the road 30 m ahead of her. Sarah's reaction time is 0.5 s. She is travelling at 20 ms^{-1}. Her maximum braking force is 10 000 N and her car (with her in it) has a mass of 850 kg.

(a) How far does she travel before applying her brakes? [2 marks]

(b) Calculate Sarah's braking distance. Assume she applies the maximum braking force until she stops. [3 marks]

(c) Does Sarah hit the cow? Justify your answer with a suitable calculation. [1 mark]

Q2 In a crash test a car slams into a solid barrier at 20 ms^{-1}. The car comes to a halt in 0.1 s. The crash test dummy goes through the windscreen and hits the barrier at a speed of 18 ms^{-1} and then also comes to a stop in 0.1 s. The mass of the car is 900 kg and the mass of the dummy is 50 kg.

(a) Calculate the forces on the car and the dummy as they are brought to a stop. [4 marks]

(b) The car is modified to include crumple zones and an airbag.
Explain what difference this will make and why. [3 marks]

Q3 Draw and label a force diagram showing a bungee jumper:
i) when they have just started falling ii) at the lowest point of their jump. [2 marks]

Crumple zone — the heap of clothes on my bedroom floor...

Being safe in a car is mainly common sense — don't drive if you're ill, drunk or just tired, and don't drive a car with dodgy brakes. But you still need to cope with exam questions, so don't go on till you understand all the stuff on these two pages.

Work and Power

As everyone knows, work in Physics isn't like normal work. It's harder. Work also has a specific meaning that's to do with movement and forces. You'll have seen this at GCSE — it just comes up in more detail for AS level.

Work is Done Whenever Energy is Transferred

This table gives you some examples of **work being done** and the **energy changes** that happen.

1) Usually you need a force to move something because you're having to **overcome another force**.
2) The thing being moved has **kinetic energy** while it's **moving**.
3) The kinetic energy is transferred to **another form of energy** when the movement stops.

ACTIVITY	WORK DONE AGAINST	FINAL ENERGY FORM
Lifting up a box.	gravity	gravitational potential energy
Pushing a chair across a level floor.	friction	heat
Pushing two magnetic north poles together.	magnetic force	magnetic energy
Stretching a spring.	stiffness of spring	elastic potential energy

The word **'work'** in Physics means the **amount of energy transferred** from one form to another when a force causes a movement of some sort.

Work = Force × Distance

When a car tows a caravan, it applies a force to the caravan to moves it to where it's wanted.
To **find out** how much **work** has been **done**, you need to use the **equation**:

work done (W) = force causing motion (F) × distance moved (s)
...where W is measured in joules (J), F is measured in newtons (N) and s is measured in metres (m).

Points to remember:

1) **Work** is the **energy** that's been **changed** from one form to another — it's not necessarily the **total** energy. E.g. moving a book from a low shelf to a higher one will increase its gravitational potential energy, but it had some potential energy to start with. Here, the **work done** would be the **increase** in potential energy, **not the total** potential energy.
2) Remember the distance needs to be measured in metres — if you have **distance in centimetres or kilometres**, you need to **convert** it to metres first.
3) The force F will be a **fixed** value in any calculations, either because it's **constant** or because it's the **average** force.
4) The equation assumes that the **direction of the force** is the **same** as the **direction of movement**.
5) The equation gives you the **definition** of the joule (symbol J): 'One joule is the work done when a force of 1 newton moves an object through a distance of 1 metre'.

The Force isn't always in the Same Direction as the Movement

Sometimes the **direction of movement** is **different** from the **direction of the force**.

Example

1) To **calculate the work done** in a situation like the one on the right, you need to consider the **horizontal** and **vertical components** of the **force**.
2) The only **movement** is in the **horizontal** direction. This means the **vertical force** is not causing any motion (and hence not doing any work) — it's just **balancing** out some of the **weight**, meaning there's a **smaller reaction force**.

3) The horizontal force is causing the motion — so to **calculate** the **work done**, this is the **only force** you need to consider. Which means we get:

$$W = Fs\cos\theta$$

Where θ is the **angle** between the **direction of the force** and the **direction of motion**. See page 16 for more on resolving forces.

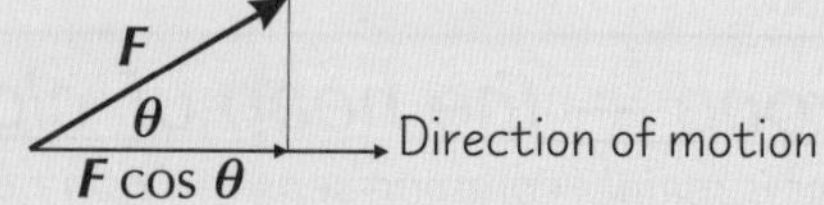

Work and Power

Power = Work Done per Second

Power means many things in everyday speech, but in physics (of course!) it has a special meaning. Power is the **rate of doing work** — in other words it is the **amount of energy transformed** from one form to another **per second.** You **calculate power** from this equation:

> **Power (P) = work done (W) / time (t)**
> ...where P is measured in watts (W), W is measured in joules (J) and t is measured in seconds (s)

The **watt** (symbol W) is defined as a **rate of energy transfer** equal to **1 joule per second**.
Yep, that's another **equation and definition** for you to **learn**.

Power is also Force × Velocity (P = Fv)

Sometimes, it's **easier** to use **this version** of the power equation. This is how you get it:

1) You **know** $P = W/t$.
2) You also **know** $W = Fs$, which gives $P = Fs/t$.
3) But $v = s/t$, which you can substitute into the above equation to give $P = Fv$.
4) It's easier to use this if you're given the **speed** in the question.
   Learn this equation as a **shortcut** to link **power** and **speed**.

Example

A car is travelling at a speed of $10\,\text{ms}^{-1}$ and is kept going against the frictional force by a driving force of 500 N in the direction of motion. Find the power supplied by the engine to keep the car moving.

Use the shortcut $P = Fv$, which gives:
$P = 500 \times 10 = 5000$ W

If the force and motion are in different directions, you can replace F with $F\cos\theta$ to get: $P = Fv\cos\theta$

You **aren't** expected to **remember** this equation, but it's made up of bits that you **are supposed to know**, so be ready for the possibility of calculating **power** in a situation where the **direction of the force and direction of motion are different**.

Practice Questions

Q1 Write down the equation used to calculate work if the force and motion are in the same direction.

Q2 Write down the equation for work if the force is at an angle to the direction of motion.

Q3 Write down the equations relating (i) power and work and (ii) power and speed.

Exam Questions

Q1 A traditional narrowboat is drawn by a horse walking along the towpath.
The horse pulls the boat at a constant speed between two locks which are 1500 m apart. The tension in the rope is 100 N at 40° to the direction of motion.

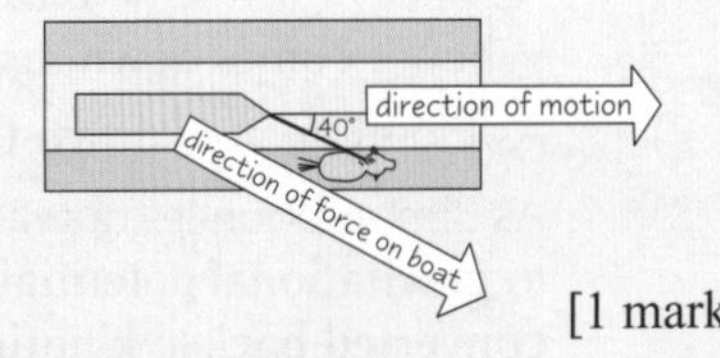

The work done on the boat is
A 114 900 J **B** 105 kJ **C** 76.6 kJ **D** 115 400 J [1 mark]

Q2 A motor is used to lift a 20 kg load a height of 3 m. (Take $g = 9.81\ \text{Nkg}^{-1}$.)
(a) Calculate the work done in lifting the load. [2 marks]
(b) The speed of the load during the lift is $0.25\ \text{ms}^{-1}$. Calculate the power delivered by the motor. [2 marks]

Work — there's just no getting away from it...

Loads of equations to learn. Well, that's what you came here for, after all. Can't beat a good bit of equation-learning, as I've heard you say quietly to yourself when you think no one's listening. Aha, can't fool me. Ahahahahahahahahahahahaha.

Conservation of Energy

__Energy__ can never be __lost__. I repeat — __energy__ can __never__ be lost. Which is basically what I'm about to take up two whole pages saying. But that's, of course, because you need to do exam questions on this as well as understand the principle.

Learn the Principle of Conservation of Energy

The **principle of conservation of energy** says that:

> Energy **cannot be created** or **destroyed.** Energy **can be transferred** from one form to another but the total amount of energy in a closed system will not change.

Example

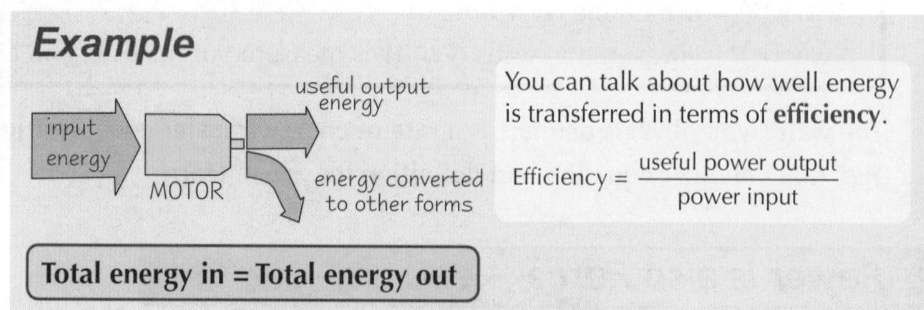

You need it for Questions about Kinetic and Potential Energy

The principle of conservation of energy nearly always comes up when you're doing questions about changes between kinetic and potential energy.

A quick reminder:

1) **Kinetic energy** is energy of anything **moving**, which you work out from $E_k = \frac{1}{2}mv^2$, where v is the velocity it's travelling at and m is its mass.
2) There are **different types of potential energy** — e.g. gravitational and elastic.
3) **Gravitational potential energy** is the energy something gains if you lift it up. You work it out using: $\Delta E_p = mg\Delta h$, where m is the mass of the object, Δh is the height it is lifted and g is the gravitational field strength (9.81 Nkg^{-1} on Earth).
4) **Elastic potential energy** (elastic stored energy) is the energy you get in, say, a stretched rubber band or spring. You work this out using $E = \frac{1}{2}ke^2$, where **e** is the extension of the spring and k is the stiffness constant.

Examples These pictures show you three **examples** of changes between kinetic and potential energy.

1) As Becky throws the **ball upwards, kinetic energy** is converted into **gravitational potential energy.** When it **comes down** again, that **gravitational potential** energy is **converted back** into **kinetic** energy.
2) As Dominic goes **down the slide, gravitational potential energy** is converted to **kinetic energy**.
3) As Simon bounces upwards from the trampoline, **elastic potential energy** is converted to **kinetic energy**, to **gravitational potential energy**. As he comes back down again, that **gravitational potential** energy is **converted back** to **kinetic** energy, to **elastic potential** energy, and so on.

In **real life** there are also **frictional forces** — Simon would have to use some **force** from his **muscles** to keep **jumping** to the **same height** above the trampoline each time. Each time the trampoline **stretches**, some **heat** is generated in the trampoline material. You're usually told to **ignore friction** in exam questions — this means you can **assume** that the **only forces** are those that provide the **potential or kinetic energy** (in this example that's **Simon's weight** and the **tension** in the springs and trampoline material).
If you're ignoring friction, you can say that the **sum of the kinetic and potential energies is constant**.

Conservation of Energy

Use Conservation of Energy to **Solve Problems**

You need to be able to **use** conservation of mechanical energy (change in potential energy = change in kinetic energy) to solve problems. The classic example is the **simple pendulum**.

In a simple pendulum, you assume that all the mass is in the **bob** at the end.

Example

A simple pendulum has a mass of 700 g and a length of 50 cm. It is pulled out to an angle of 30° from the vertical.

(a) Find the gravitational potential energy stored in the pendulum bob.

Start by drawing a diagram.

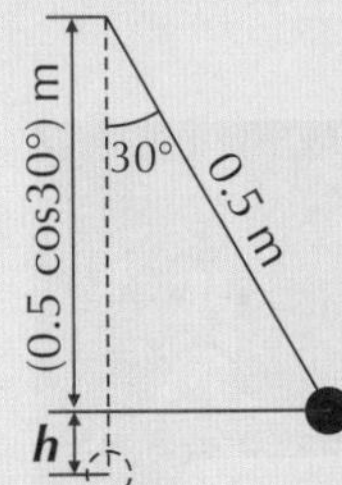

You can work out the increase in height, ***h***, of the end of the pendulum using trig.

Gravitational potential energy = ***mgh***

$= 0.7 \times 9.81 \times (0.5 - 0.5\cos 30°)$

$= 0.46$ J

(b) The pendulum is released. Find the maximum speed of the pendulum bob as it passes the vertical position.

To find the *maximum* speed, assume no air resistance, then $mgh = \frac{1}{2}mv^2$.

Cancel the ***m***s and rearrange to give: $v^2 = 2gh$

$= 2 \times 9.81 \times (0.5 - 0.5\cos 30°)$

$= 1.31429...$

$v = 1.15$ ms^{-1}

You could be asked to apply this stuff to just about any situation in the exam. **Rollercoasters** are a bit of a favourite.

Practice Questions

Q1 State the principle of conservation of energy.

Q2 What are the equations for calculating kinetic energy and gravitational potential energy?

Q3 Show that, if there's no air resistance and the mass of the string is negligible, the speed of a pendulum is independent of the mass of the bob.

Exam Questions

Q1 A skateboarder is on a half-pipe. He lets the board run down one side of the ramp and up the other. The height of the ramp is 2 m. Take **g** as 9.81 Nkg^{-1}.

(a) If you assume that there is no friction, what would be his speed at the lowest point of the ramp? [3 marks]

(b) How high will he rise up the other side? [1 mark]

(c) Real ramps are not frictionless, so what must the skater do to reach the top on the other side? [1 mark]

Q2 A 20 g rubber ball is released from a height of 8 m. (Assume that the effect of air resistance is negligible.)

(a) Find the kinetic energy of the ball just before it hits the ground. [2 marks]

(b) The ball strikes the ground and rebounds to a height of 6.5 m. How much energy is converted to heat and sound in the impact with the ground? [2 marks]

Energy is never lost — it just sometimes prefers the scenic route...

Remember to check your answers — I can't count the number of times I've forgotten to square the velocities or to multiply by the ½... I reckon it's definitely worth the extra minute to check.

Hooke's Law

Hooke's law doesn't apply to all materials, and only works for the rest up to a point, but it's still pretty handy.

Hooke's Law Says that Extension is Proportional to Force

If a **metal wire** is supported at the top and then a weight attached to the bottom, it **stretches**. The weight pulls down with force ***F***, producing an equal and opposite force at the support.

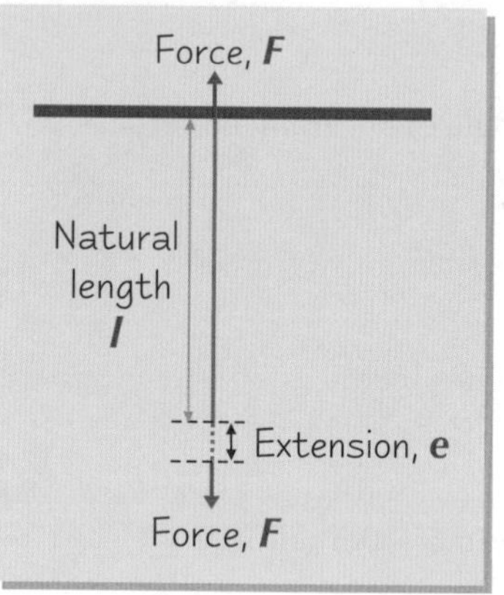

1) **Robert Hooke** discovered in 1676 that the extension of a stretched wire, **e**, is proportional to the load or force, ***F***. This relationship is now called **Hooke's law**.
2) Hooke's law can be written:

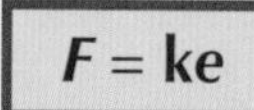

$$F = ke$$

Where **k** is a constant that depends on the material being stretched. **k** is called the **stiffness constant**.

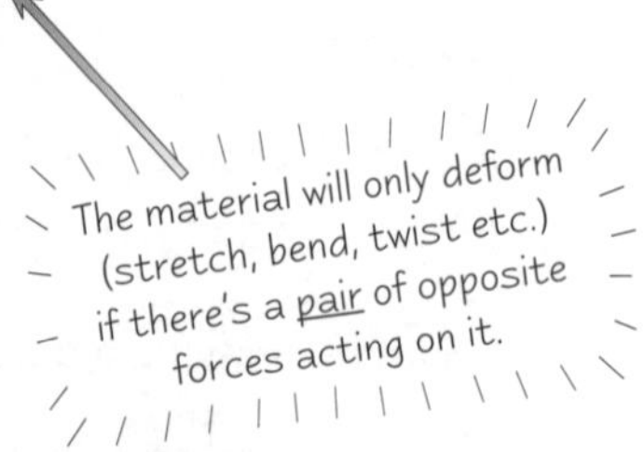

Hooke's Law Also Applies to Springs

A metal spring also changes length when you apply a **pair of opposite forces**.

1) The **extension** or **compression** of a spring is **proportional** to the **force** applied — so Hooke's law applies.
2) For springs, **k** in the formula ***F* = ke** is usually called the **spring stiffness** or **spring constant**.

Hooke's law works just as well for **compressive** forces as **tensile** forces. For a spring, **k** has the **same value** whether the forces are tensile or compressive (that's not true for all materials).

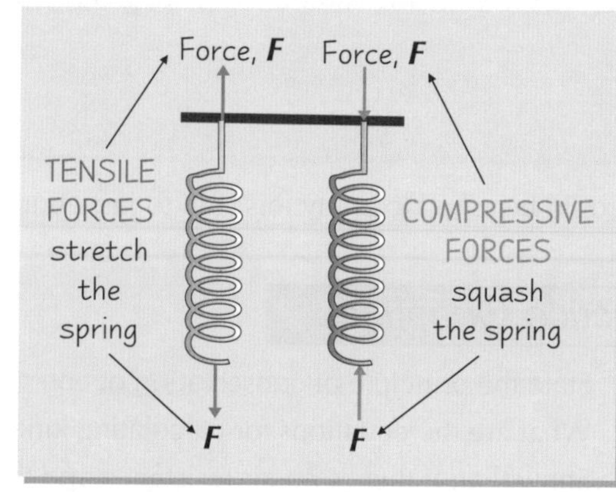

Hooke's Law Stops Working when the Load is Great Enough

There's a **limit** to the force you can apply for Hooke's law to stay true.

1) The graph shows load against extension for a **typical metal wire**.
2) The first part of the graph shows Hooke's law being obeyed — there's a **straight-line relationship** between **load** and **extension**.
3) When the load becomes great enough, the graph starts to **curve**. The point marked E on the graph is called the **elastic limit**.
4) If you increase the load past the elastic limit, the material will be **permanently stretched**. When all the force is removed, the material will be **longer** than at the start.
5) **Metals** generally obey Hooke's law up to the limit of proportionality, which is very near the elastic limit.
6) Be careful — there are some materials, like **rubber**, that only obey Hooke's law for **really small** extensions.

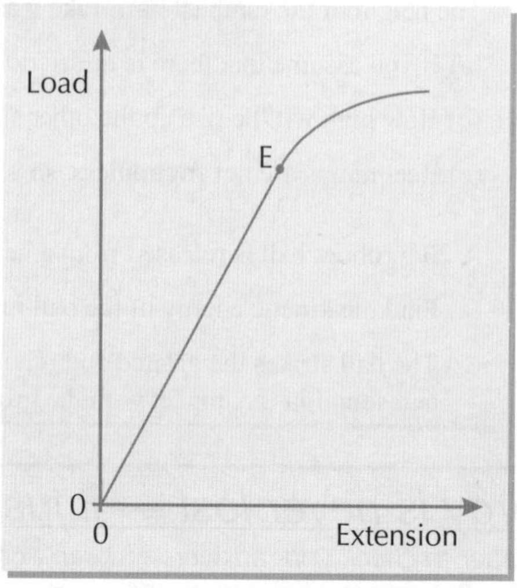

Hooke's Law

So basically...

A Stretch can be **Elastic** or **Plastic**

Elastic

If a **deformation** is **elastic**, the material returns to its **original shape** once the forces are removed.

1) When the material is put under **tension**, the **atoms** of the material are **pulled apart** from one another.
2) Atoms can **move** small distances relative to their **equilibrium positions**, without actually changing position in the material.
3) Once the **load** is **removed**, the atoms **return** to their **equilibrium** distance apart.

For a metal, elastic deformation happens as long as **Hooke's law** is obeyed.

Plastic

If a deformation is **plastic**, the material is **permanently stretched**.

1) Some atoms in the material move position relative to one another.
2) When the load is removed, the **atoms don't return** to their original positions.

A metal stretched **past its elastic limit** shows plastic deformation.

Practice Questions

Q1 State Hooke's law.

Q2 Define tensile forces and compressive forces.

Q3 Explain what is meant by the elastic limit of a material.

Q4 From studying the force-extension graph for a material as it is loaded and unloaded, how can you tell:
(a) if Hooke's law is being obeyed,
(b) if the elastic limit has been reached?

Q5 What is plastic behaviour of a material under load?

Exam Questions

Q1 A metal guitar string stretches 4.0 mm when a 10 N force is applied.

(a) If the string obeys Hooke's law, how far will the string stretch with a 15 N force? [1 mark]

(b) Calculate the stiffness constant for this string in Nm^{-1}. [2 marks]

(c) The string is tightened beyond its elastic limit. What would be noticed about the string? [1 mark]

Q2 A rubber band is 6.0 cm long. When it is loaded with 2.5 N, its length becomes 10.4 cm.
Further loading increases the length to 16.2 cm when the force is 5.0 N.

Does the rubber band obey Hooke's law when the force on it is 5.0 N?
Justify your answer with a suitable calculation. [2 marks]

Sod's Law — if you don't learn it, it'll be in the exam...

Three things you didn't know about Robert Hooke — he was the first person to use the word 'cell' (in terms of biology, not prisons), he helped Christopher Wren with his designs for St Paul's Cathedral and no one knows quite what he looked like. I'd like to think that if I did all that stuff, then someone would at least remember what I looked like — poor old Hooke.

Stress and Strain

How much a material stretches for a particular applied force depends on its dimensions.
If you want to compare the properties of two different materials, you need to use stress and strain instead.
A stress-strain graph is the same for any sample of a particular material — the size of the sample doesn't matter.

A Stress Causes a Strain

A material subjected to a pair of **opposite forces** might **deform**, i.e. **change shape**. If the forces **stretch** the material, they're **tensile**. If the forces **squash** the material, they're **compressive**.

1) **Tensile stress** is defined as the **force applied**, ***F***, divided by the **cross-sectional area**, ***A***:

$$\text{stress} = \frac{F}{A}$$

The **units** of stress are $\mathbf{Nm^{-2}}$ or pascals, **Pa**.

2) **Tensile strain** is defined as the **change in length**, i.e. the **extension**, divided by the **original length** of the material:

$$\text{strain} = \frac{e}{l}$$

Strain has **no units** — it's just a **number**.

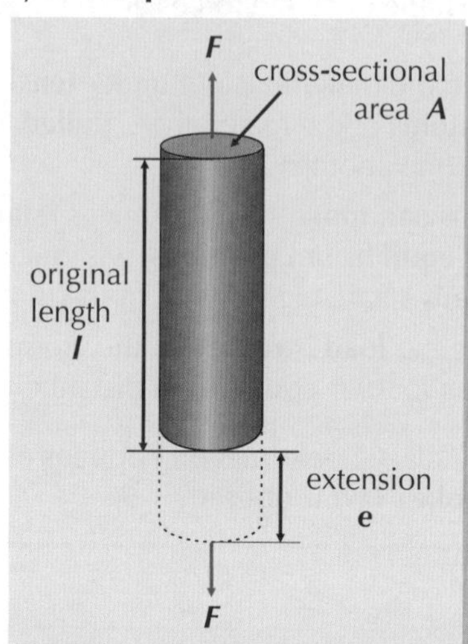

3) It doesn't matter whether the forces producing the **stress** and **strain** are **tensile** or **compressive** — the **same equations** apply. The only difference is that you tend to think of **tensile** forces as **positive**, and **compressive** forces as **negative**.

A Stress Big Enough to Break the Material is Called the Breaking Stress

As a greater and greater tensile **force** is applied to a material, the **stress** on it **increases**.

1) The effect of the **stress** is to start to **pull** the **atoms apart** from one another.
2) Eventually the stress becomes **so great** that atoms **separate completely**, and the **material breaks**. This is shown by point **B** on the graph. The stress at which this occurs is called the **breaking stress**.
3) The point marked **UTS** on the graph is called the **ultimate tensile stress**. This is the **maximum stress** that the material can withstand.
4) **Engineers** have to consider the **UTS** and **breaking stress** of materials when designing a **structure**.

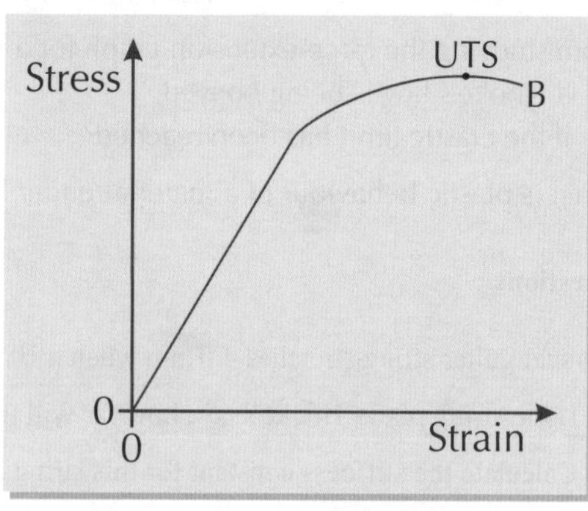

Elastic Strain Energy is the Energy Stored in a Stretched Material

When a material is **stretched**, **work** has to be done in stretching the material.

1) **Before** the **elastic limit**, **all** the **work done** in stretching is **stored** as **potential energy** in the material.
2) This stored energy is called **elastic strain energy**.
3) On a **graph** of **force against extension**, the elastic strain energy is given by the **area under the graph**.

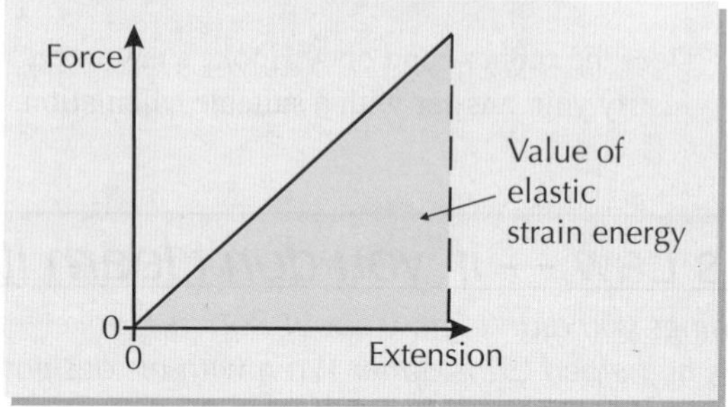

Stress and Strain

You can Calculate the **Energy Stored** in a **Stretched Wire**

Provided a material obeys Hooke's law, the **potential energy** stored inside it can be **calculated** quite easily.

1) The work done on the wire in stretching it is equal to the energy stored.
2) **Work done** equals **force × displacement**.
3) However, the **force** on the material **isn't constant**. It rises from zero up to force ***F***.
   To calculate the **work done**, use the average force between zero and ***F***, i.e. ½***F***.

   work done = ½F × **e**

4) Then the **elastic strain energy**, ***E***, is:

   $E = \frac{1}{2}Fe$

   This is the triangular area under the force-extension graph — see previous page.

5) Because Hooke's law is being obeyed, ***F* = *ke***,
   which means ***F*** can be replaced in the equation to give:

   $E = \frac{1}{2}ke^2$

6) If the material is stretched beyond the **elastic limit**, some work is done separating atoms.
   This will **not** be **stored** as strain energy and so isn't available when the force is released.

Practice Questions

Q1 Write a definition for tensile stress.

Q2 Explain what is meant by the tensile strain on a material.

Q3 What is meant by the breaking stress of a material?

Q4 How can the elastic strain energy be found from the force against extension graph of a material under load?

Q5 The work done is usually calculated as force multiplied by displacement.
Explain why the work done in stretching a wire is ½*Fe*.

Exam Questions

Q1 A steel wire is 2.00 m long. When a 300 N force is applied to the wire, it stretches 4.0 mm.
The wire has a circular cross-section with a diameter of 1.0 mm.

(a) What is the cross-sectional area of the wire? [1 mark]

(b) Calculate the tensile stress in the wire. [1 mark]

(c) Calculate the tensile strain of the wire. [1 mark]

Q2 A copper wire (which obeys Hooke's law) is stretched by 3.0 mm when a force of 50 N is applied.

(a) Calculate the stiffness constant for this wire in Nm^{-1}. [2 marks]

(b) What is the value of the elastic strain energy in the stretched wire? [1 mark]

Q3 A pinball machine contains a spring which is used to fire a small, 12 g metal ball to start the game.
The spring has a stiffness constant of 40.8 Nm^{-1}. It is compressed by 5 cm and then released to fire the ball.
The maximum possible speed of the ball is

A 1.86 ms^{-1} **B** 2.92 ms^{-1} **C** 4.12 ms^{-1} **D** 8.50 ms^{-1} [1 mark]

UTS a laugh a minute, this stuff...

Here endeth the proper physics for a few pages — you're stuck with a bit of materials science (and I don't care what your exam board says). It's all a bit "useful" for my liking. Calls itself a physics course... grumble... grumble... wasn't like this in my day... But to be fair — some of it's quite interesting, and you've got all the fun of fluids coming up on page 34.

The Young Modulus

Busy chap, Thomas Young. He did this work on tensile stress as something of a sideline. Light was his main thing. He proved that light behaved like a wave, explained how we see in colour and worked out what causes astigmatism.

The Young Modulus is Stress ÷ Strain

When you apply a **load** to stretch a material, it experiences a **tensile stress** and a **tensile strain**.

1) Up to a point called the **limit of proportionality** (see p.33), the stress and strain of a material are proportional to each other.
2) So below this limit, for a particular material, stress divided by strain is a constant. This constant is called the **Young modulus**, ***E***.

$$E = \frac{\text{tensile stress}}{\text{tensile strain}} = \frac{F/A}{e/l} = \frac{Fl}{eA}$$

Where, F = force in N, A = cross-sectional area in m^2, l = initial length in m and e = extension in m.

3) The **units** of the Young modulus are the same as stress (**Nm^{-2}** or pascals), since strain has no units.
4) The Young modulus is used by **engineers** to make sure their materials can withstand sufficient forces.

To Find the Young Modulus, You need a Very Long Wire

This is the experiment you're most likely to do in class:

Mum moment: if you're doing this experiment, wear safety goggles — if the wire snaps, it could get very messy...

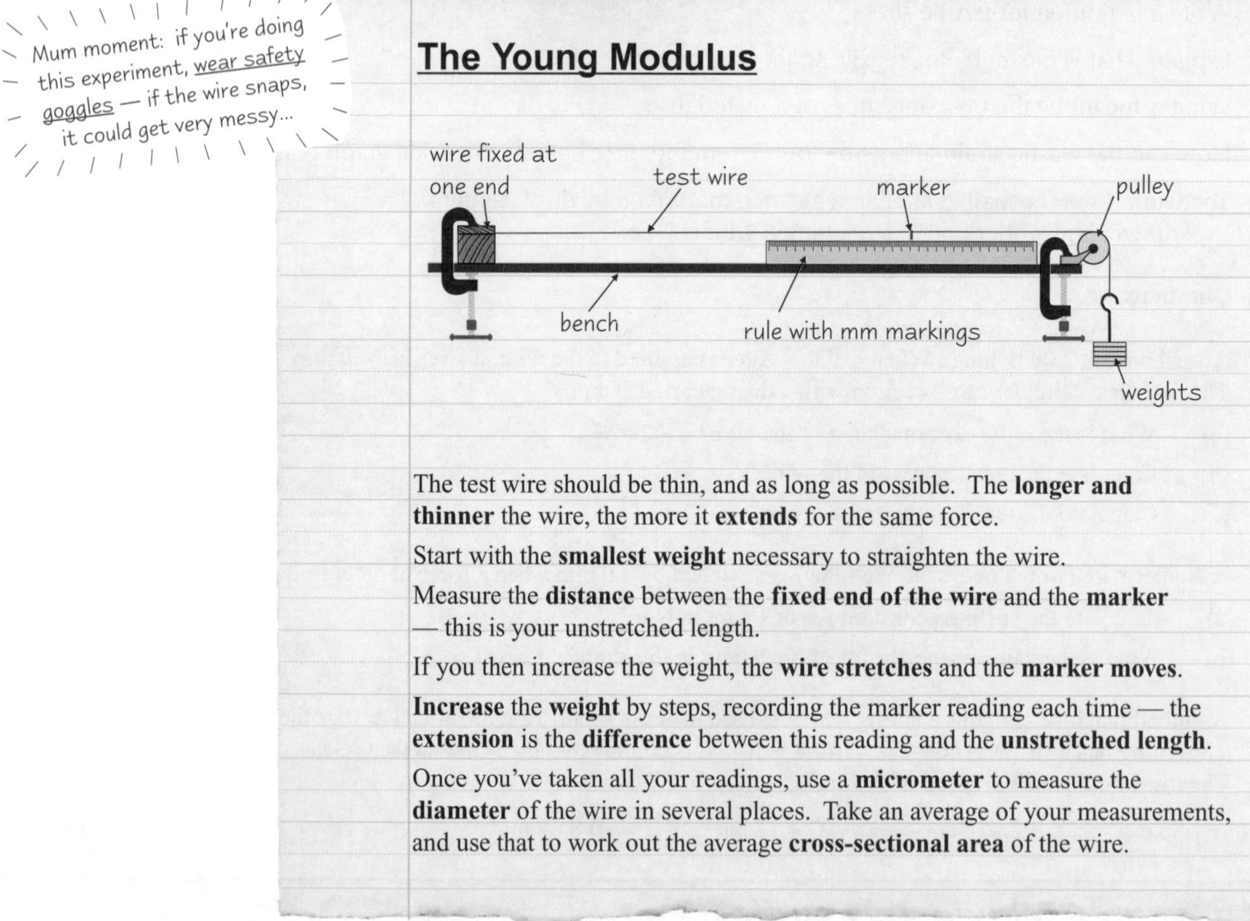

The test wire should be thin, and as long as possible. The **longer and thinner** the wire, the more it **extends** for the same force.

Start with the **smallest weight** necessary to straighten the wire.

Measure the **distance** between the **fixed end of the wire** and the **marker** — this is your unstretched length.

If you then increase the weight, the **wire stretches** and the **marker moves**.

Increase the **weight** by steps, recording the marker reading each time — the **extension** is the **difference** between this reading and the **unstretched length**.

Once you've taken all your readings, use a **micrometer** to measure the **diameter** of the wire in several places. Take an average of your measurements, and use that to work out the average **cross-sectional area** of the wire.

The other standard way of measuring the Young modulus in the lab is using **Searle's apparatus**. This is a bit more accurate, but it's harder to do and the equipment's more complicated.

The Young Modulus

Use a Stress-Strain Graph to Find E

You can plot a **graph** of **stress against strain** from your results.

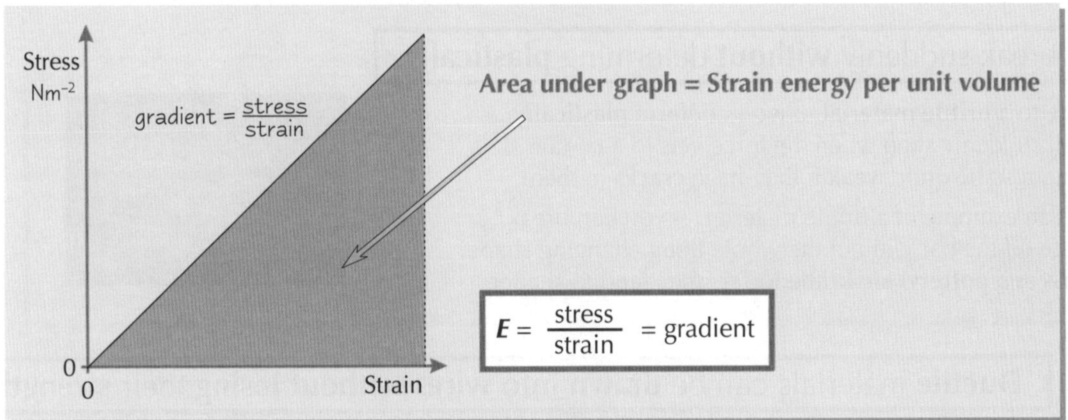

1) The **gradient** of the graph gives the Young modulus, **E**.
2) The **area under the graph** gives the **strain energy** (or energy stored) per unit volume i.e. the energy stored per 1 m^3 of wire.
3) The stress-strain graph is a **straight line** provided that Hooke's law is obeyed, so you can also calculate the energy per unit volume as:

energy = ½ × stress × strain

Practice Questions

Q1 Define the Young modulus for a material.

Q2 What are the units for the Young modulus?

Q3 Explain why a thin test wire is used to find the Young modulus.

Q4 What is given by the area contained under a stress-strain graph?

Exam Questions

Q1 A steel wire is stretched elastically. For a load of 80 N, the wire extends by 3.6 mm. The original length of the wire was 2.50 m and its average diameter is 0.6 mm.

(a) Calculate the cross-sectional area of the wire in m^2. [1 mark]

(b) Find the tensile stress applied to the wire. [1 mark]

(c) Calculate the tensile strain of the wire. [1 mark]

(d) What is the value of the Young modulus for steel? [1 mark]

Q2 The Young modulus for copper is 1.3×10^{11} Nm^{-2}.

(a) If the stress on a copper wire is 2.6×10^{8} Nm^{-2}, what is the strain? [2 marks]

(b) If the load applied to the copper wire is 100 N, what is the cross-sectional area of the wire? [1 mark]

(c) Calculate the strain energy per unit volume for this loaded wire. [1 mark]

Learn that experiment — it's important...

Getting back to the good Dr Young... As if ground-breaking work in light, the physics of vision and materials science wasn't enough, he was also a well-respected physician, a linguist and an Egyptologist. He was one of the first to try to decipher the Rosetta stone (he didn't get it right, but nobody's perfect). Makes you feel kind of inferior, doesn't it. Best get learning.

Behaviour of Solids

If you want to be able to describe a solid properly, you need to know what all the terms mean.

Terms to Describe the **Behaviour of Solids** Have **Precise Meanings**

Brittle materials break suddenly **without** deforming **plastically**.

If you apply a **force** to a **brittle material**, it won't **deform plastically** (see p. 27), but will suddenly **snap** when the force gets to a certain size. Brittle materials can also be quite **weak** if they have **cracks** in them.

A **chocolate bar** is an example of a brittle material — you can break chunks of chocolate off the bar without the whole thing changing shape. **Ceramics** (e.g. **glass** and **pottery**) are brittle too — they tend to shatter.

Ductile materials can be **drawn into wires without losing** their **strength**.

You can change the **shape** of **ductile materials** by drawing them into **wires** or other shapes. The important thing is that they **keep their strength** when they're deformed like this.

Copper is ductile, and with its high electrical conductivity this means that it's ideal for **electric wires**. A **ductile material** has been used for the cables supporting the **ski lift** in the photo — it's been drawn into long wires, but kept its strength.

Malleable materials change **shape** but may **lose** their **strength**.

The shape of **malleable materials** can be changed fairly easily, e.g. by **hammering** or **rolling**. The difference between malleable and ductile materials is that **malleable** materials **won't** necessarily **keep their strength**.

Gold is an example of a malleable metal — you can change the shape of a gold ring using just your fingers. **Brass** is malleable too — it can be bent and stretched into **complex shapes** to make musical instruments.

Hard materials are very **resistant** to **cutting**, **indentation** and **abrasion**.

If you try to cut, dent or scratch a hard material, you'll probably have very little effect. Their structure means **hard materials** are **resistant** to **cutting**, **indentation** (becoming dented) and **abrasion** (scratching).

Cutting tools (e.g. chisels) need to be harder than the stuff they're cutting — they're often made from **hardened steel**. **Diamond** is just about the hardest material there is — it's often used to reinforce the tips of drill bits.

Stiff materials have a **high resistance** to **bending** and **stretching**.

Changing the shape of **stiff materials** is really difficult as they are **resistant** to both **bending** and **stretching**. Stiffness is measured by the **Young modulus** (see p. 30) — the higher the value, the stiffer the material.

The outer protective casing of **safety helmets** and **safety boots** need to be very stiff so that they keep their shape and don't **crush** onto your body when something impacts on them.

Tough materials are really **difficult to break**.

Toughness is a measure of the **energy** a material can **absorb** before it breaks. Really **tough materials** can absorb a lot of energy so are very **difficult** to **break**.

Some **polymers**, including certain types of **polythene**, are very tough. The hull of this **kayak** is made of a tough material so it won't break on rocks.

Behaviour of Solids

Do you remember that lovely stress-strain graph from page 28? Well, it turns out that because different solids have different properties, their stress-strain graphs look different too.

Stress-Strain Graphs for *Ductile* Materials *Curve*

The diagram shows a **stress-strain graph** for a typical **ductile** material — e.g. a copper wire.

Point **Y** is the **yield point** — here the material suddenly starts to **stretch** without any extra load. The **yield point** (or yield stress) is the **stress** at which a large amount of **plastic deformation** takes place with a **constant** or **reduced load.**

Point E is the **elastic limit** — at this point the material starts to behave **plastically**. From point E onwards, the material would **no longer** return to its **original shape** once the stress was removed.

Point **P** is the **limit of proportionality** — after this, the graph is no longer a straight line but starts to **bend**. At this point, the material **stops** obeying **Hooke's law**, but would still **return** to its **original shape** if the stress was removed.

Before point P, the graph is a **straight line** through the **origin**. This shows that the material is obeying **Hooke's law** (page 26).

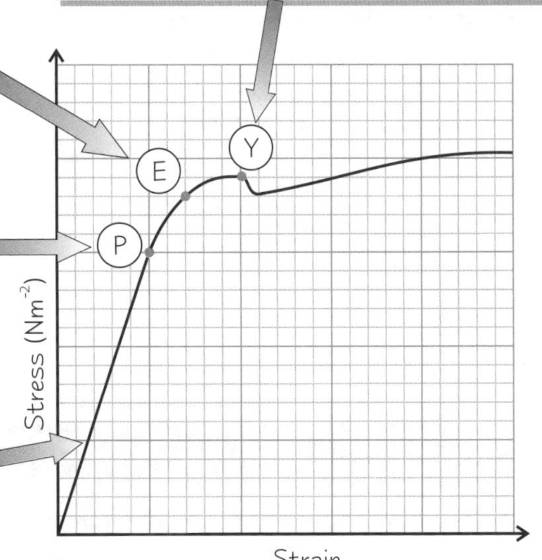

Practice Questions

Q1 What is the difference between the limit of proportionality and the elastic limit?

Q2 Sketch stress-strain graphs of typical ductile, brittle and polymeric materials and describe their shapes.

Exam Questions

Q1 Which of the following best describes a material which can be easily shaped without losing strength, and is resistant to tearing?

A ductile, stiff and tough
B malleable and hard
C malleable, ductile and tough
D malleable, ductile and stiff [1 mark]

Q2 Hardened steel is a hard, brittle form of steel made by heating it up slowly and then quenching it in cold water.
Write down one application in which hardened steel could be used.
Explain why it would be useful in this context. [2 marks]

Q3 Riding helmets are designed to protect a rider's head from injury should they fall off their horse.
Describe three properties of a material that would be suitable for a riding helmet.
Explain why each of these properties is advantageous. [6 marks]

My brain must be stiff — it's resistant to being stretched...

Those material scientists are a tricky lot — you go all your life thinking you know what hard means (who doesn't?), then they come along and say, 'that's not good enough — you need to know the proper meaning'. They've got a point though — saying, 'hard... well, it's err... not soft' isn't going to get you any marks. Go on — learn them all. It'll be good fun... honest.

Streamlines and Flow

Solids are quite good fun, but you're in for a treat now — it's time to learn all about fluids...

Streamlines are Stable Flowlines

1) **Fluids** are things that **flow** — i.e. **liquids** and **gases**.
2) When a fluid flows, **different parts** of it may move in **different directions** and at **different rates**.
3) It's useful to think of a fluid as made up of '**fluid elements**'. A **fluid element** is a part of the fluid in which all the particles are flowing in the **same direction** at the **same rate** — i.e. with the **same velocity**.
4) Each fluid element is **small** enough that it flows **without breaking up**, but **large** enough that you don't have to consider the **random movement** (thermal motion) of the **particles** within it.
5) The **path** that a particular **fluid element** follows is called a **flowline**.
6) If **every element** on a flowline follows the **same path**, then the flowline is said to be **stable** because it does not move about. A **stable flowline** is called a **streamline**.

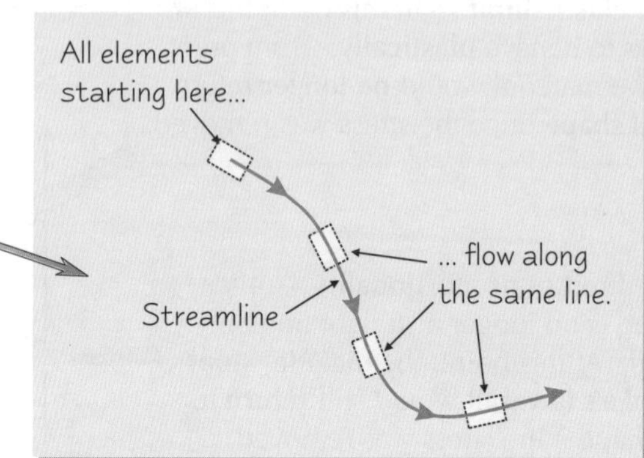

Streamlines are Parallel in Laminar Flow

1) **Laminar flow** is a flow **pattern** where all the **fluid elements** flow in the **same direction**.
2) The result of this is that all the flowlines are **streamlines** that run **parallel** to each another.
3) **Laminar flow** usually occurs when a fluid is **flowing slowly**.

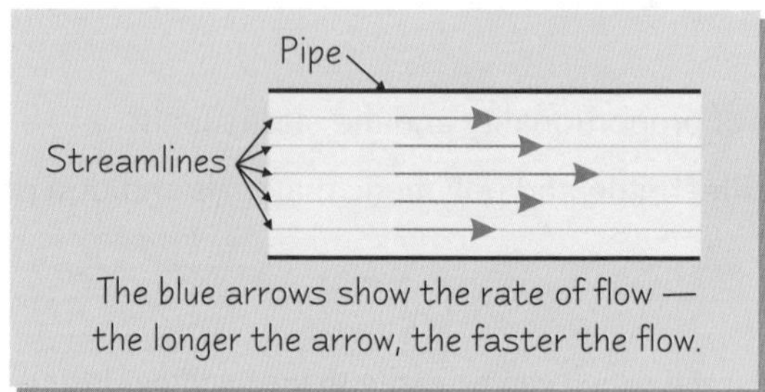

The blue arrows show the rate of flow — the longer the arrow, the faster the flow.

4) The diagram shows water undergoing **laminar flow** in a **pipe**. The streamlines **all** run along the length of the pipe.

What do you get if you cross a baby sheep with a river? A lamb in a flow.

Flowlines are Unstable in Turbulent Flow

1) **Turbulent flow** is a different flow **pattern** where the **fluid elements** get **mixed up**. You can't draw **streamlines** if the flow is turbulent because the flowlines are **unstable** (they keep changing).
2) **Turbulent flow** usually occurs when a **fluid** is flowing **quickly**.
3) In turbulent flow, the fluid often moves around in **miniature whirlpools** — called **eddy currents**.

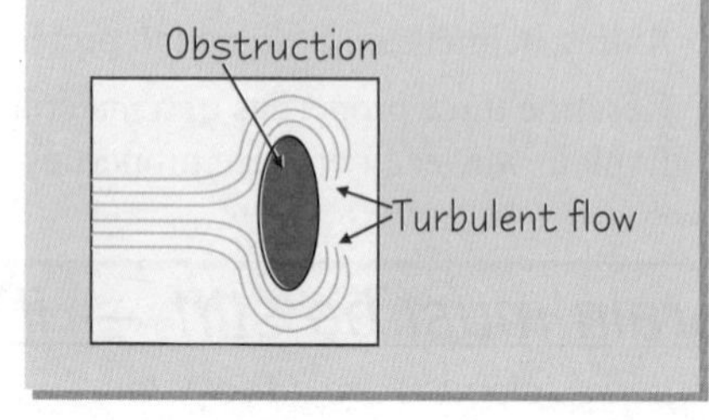

Streamlines and Flow

Both Types of Flow are Used in Manufacturing

1) **Both** types of flow (laminar and turbulent) are used in **manufacturing**.
2) For example, **laminar flow** is needed if the fluid needs to flow **smoothly** (e.g. through pipes) and with a **minimum** amount of **viscous drag** (see below).
3) **Turbulent flow** is needed if fluids need to be thoroughly **mixed** (e.g. mixing chemicals or food ingredients).

Viscous Drag — the Force of Friction Produced by a Flowing Fluid

1) When fluid elements move **past** each other with **different velocities** there is a **force of friction** between them. Friction opposes motion, so the force acts to **slow** the flow.

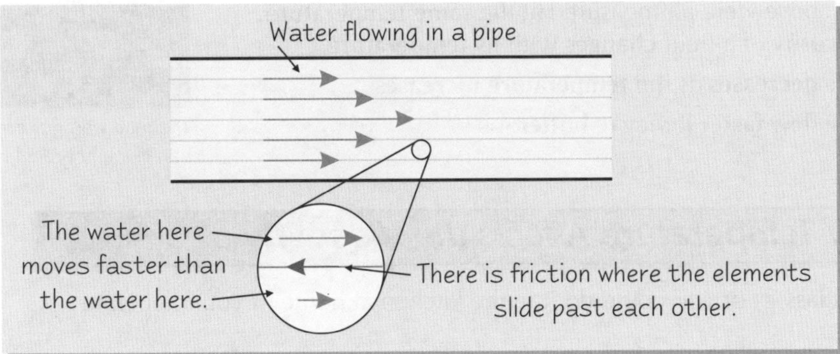

2) The **force of friction** produced by a flowing fluid is called **viscous drag**.
3) The **size** of the force depends on the **viscosity** of the fluid (more about that on the next page) — the **higher the viscosity**, the **larger the force**.
4) **Viscous drag** is much **larger** when the flow is **turbulent**.

Practice Questions

Q1 What is a streamline?

Q2 What is meant by laminar flow?

Q3 Draw a streamline diagram of a fluid undergoing laminar flow.

Q4 Why couldn't you draw a similar diagram to illustrate turbulent flow?

Exam Question

Q1 In a chocolate factory, melted chocolate flows through a pipe into a large container where it is mixed with other ingredients.

(a) Using a diagram, describe the flow of the chocolate in the pipe. [4 marks]

(b) When the chocolate is in the pipe, it flows fairly slowly. Explain why this happens. [2 marks]

(c) Describe how the flow changes when the chocolate enters the mixing container. [2 marks]

I know a guy called Eddy Current — he's always giving things a whirl...

Sorry about the 'lamb-in-a-flow' joke — it really is awful. My friend Joe thought it up, I'm just not that funny. The important things to learn on these pages are all the terms — streamline, flowline, laminar flow, turbulent flow, viscous drag. If you're having trouble remembering them, try explaining them to someone else (little brothers are useful for this) — it really helps.

Viscosity

Some fluids are thicker than others...

Rate of Flow Depends on Viscosity

The table shows the **viscosity** of four different fluids and the **rate** at which they **flowed** through a pipe. The **diameter** of the pipe and the **temperature** and **pressure** within the pipe were the **same** for all the fluids.

The table shows that the **higher the viscosity** of a fluid, the **slower it flowed** through the pipe. In other words, the **rate of flow** of a fluid **depends** on its **viscosity**.

Fluid	Viscosity (Nsm^{-2})	Rate of flow (m^3s^{-1})
Gasoline	2.8×10^{-4}	2.72
Water	1.1×10^{-3}	0.83
Kerosene	2.0×10^{-3}	0.68
Crude oil	9.8×10^{-3}	0.08

Viscosity Depends on Temperature

The **viscosities** given in the table above were all measured at the **same temperature**. This is important because the **viscosity** of a fluid **changes** with its **temperature**.

1) The **viscosity** of most fluids **decreases** as the **temperature increases**.
2) This means fluids generally **flow faster** if they're **hotter**.

The mud was more viscous than Humphrey had realised.

You Can Measure How Temperature Affects the Viscosity of a Fluid

You might try this experiment in class — or you could do it in the kitchen at home (if you happen to have a dropping funnel to hand):

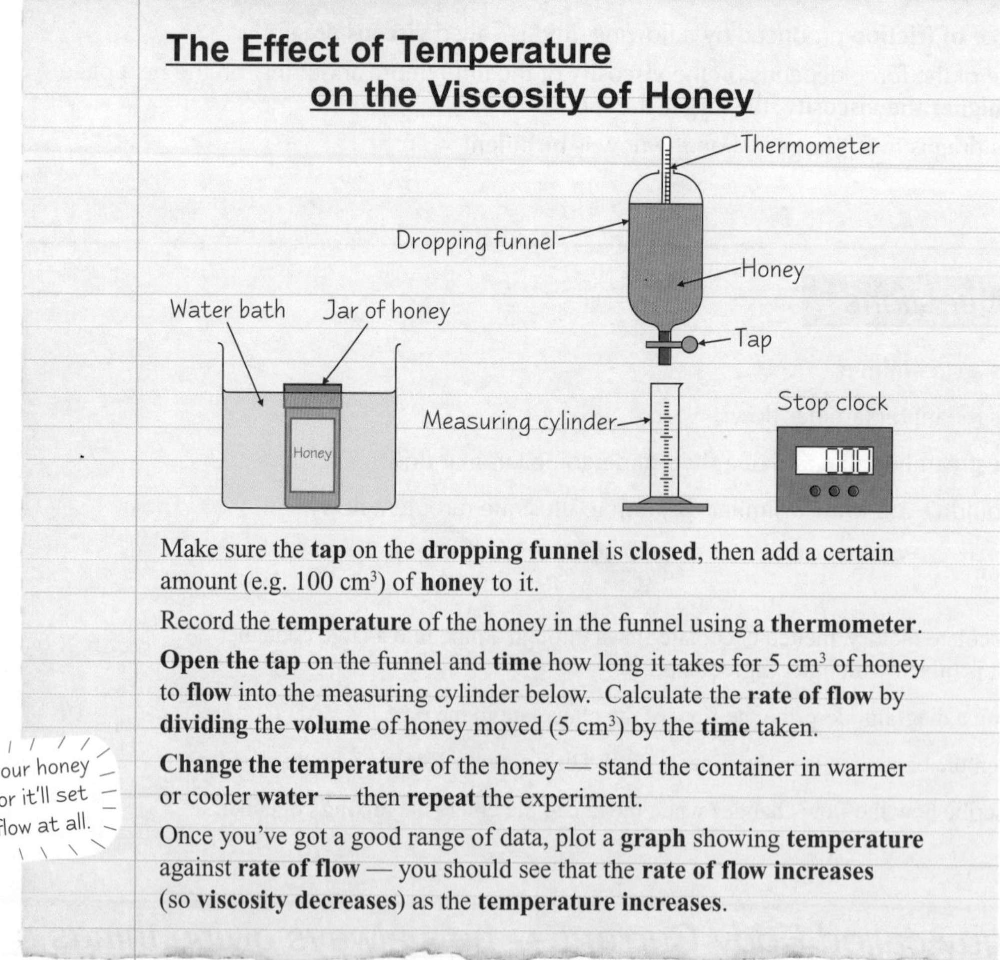

Don't cool your honey too much, or it'll set and won't flow at all.

Another way of investigating the effect of temperature on the viscosity of a liquid is to use an **Ostwald viscometer** to measure the **viscosity** of the liquid at different **temperatures** — if you've got one handy of course.

Viscosity

Viscous Drag Acts on Objects Moving Through Fluids

When an object moves through a fluid, you get **friction** between the surface of the **object** and the **fluid**. This is **viscous drag** — it's the same effect as the friction between fluid elements that move past each other (p. 35). You can calculate the **force due to viscous drag** on a **spherical** object moving through a fluid using **Stokes' law**.

Stokes' law can be written as:

$$F = 6\pi \eta r v$$

F is the **viscous drag** (N), η (eta) is the **viscosity** of the fluid (Nsm^{-2} or Pa·s), ***r*** is the **radius** of the object (m) and ***v*** is the **speed** the object is moving at (ms^{-1}).

Fluids Exert Upthrust on Immersed Objects

1) When you **float** an object on water, the **weight** of the object is **balanced** by an **opposing force** from the water. If you try to push the object under the water, it will **spring back** to the surface as soon as you let go. The **force** that 'pushes' the object **upwards** is called **upthrust** — it's caused by **fluid pressure**.
2) **Fluid pressure** is an **outward force** exerted on all **surfaces** the fluid is in contact with — including the surfaces of anything **immersed** in it. It's **caused** by the **weight** of the fluid — which means it **increases** with depth. The **deeper** you go into the fluid, the **greater** the **weight** of fluid above you, so the **greater** the **pressure**.
3) The result is that the **fluid pressure** is **higher** at the **bottom** of the object than at the top. This difference in pressure results in a **net upward force** on the object, as shown in the diagram. This force is the **upthrust**.
4) The size of the **upthrust** is **equal** to the **weight** of the **fluid displaced** by the object — this is **Archimedes' principle** and it's true for **all fluids**.

Upthrust = weight of fluid displaced

Practice Questions

Q1 How does the rate of flow of a fluid depend on its viscosity?

Q2 How does the rate of flow of most fluids depend on their temperature?

Exam Questions

Q1 A student dropped a marble into a measuring cylinder full of water. The marble sank slowly to the bottom.

(a) Draw a diagram of the marble falling through the water and label the three forces that are acting on it. [3 marks]

(b) If the marble was falling at constant speed then what was the resultant force acting on it? [1 mark]

(c) Use the following data to work out the speed that the marble was falling (at its terminal velocity).

Radius of marble = 5.0×10^{-3} m
Mass of marble = 5×10^{-5} kg
Mass of water displaced = 2.1×10^{-5} kg
Gravitational field strength = 9.81 Nkg^{-1}.
Viscosity of water = 0.0011 Nsm^{-2} [6 marks]

Q2 When oil is piped over long distances, it tends to flow more slowly during the night than during the day. Explain why this happens. [3 marks]

Finding viscosity a drag? You need upthrust — it's a real boost...

If you can read this you clearly haven't tried the investigation on the last page — or else you were smart enough to put the book away before you covered it in honey. Mmm... honey... Sorry where was I, oh yes, fluids — very important, learn it all.

The Nature of Waves

Aaaah... playing with slinky springs and waggling ropes about. It's all good clean fun as my mate Richard used to say...

A **Wave Transfers Energy** Away from Its Source

A **progressive** (moving) wave carries **energy** from one place to another **without transferring any material**. Here are some ways you can tell waves carry energy:

1) Electromagnetic waves cause things to **heat up**.
2) **X-rays** and **gamma** rays knock electrons out of their orbits, causing **ionisation**.
3) Loud **sounds** make things **vibrate**.
4) **Wave power** can be used to **generate electricity**.
5) Since waves carry energy away, the **source** of the wave **loses energy**.

Here are all the **bits** of a **Wave** you Need to Know

1) **Displacement**, ***X***, metres — how far a **point** on the wave has **moved** from its **undisturbed position**.
2) **Amplitude**, **a**, metres — **maximum displacement**.
3) **Wavelength**, **λ**, metres — the **length** of **one whole wave**, from **crest** to **crest** or **trough** to **trough**.

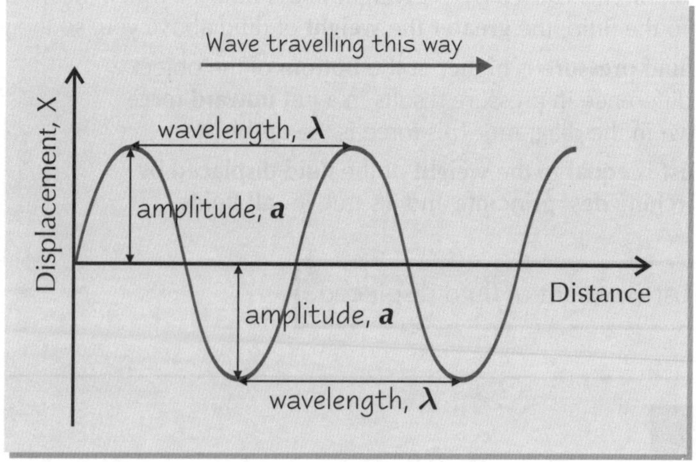

4) **Period**, ***T***, seconds — the **time taken** for a **whole vibration**.
5) **Frequency**, ***f***, hertz — the **number** of **vibrations per second** passing a given **point**.
6) **Phase difference** — the amount by which **one** wave **lags behind another** wave. **Measured** in **degrees** or **radians**. See page 48.

Waves Can Be **Reflected** and **Refracted**

Reflection — the wave is **bounced back** when it **hits a boundary**. E.g. you can see the reflection of light in mirrors. The reflection of water waves can be demonstrated in a ripple tank.

Refraction — the wave **changes direction** as it enters a **different medium**. The change in direction is a result of the wave slowing down or speeding up.

The **Frequency** is the **Inverse** of the **Period**

$$\textit{Frequency} = \frac{1}{\textit{period}}$$

It's that simple.
Get the **units** straight: **1 Hz = 1 s^{-1}**.

The Nature of Waves

Wave Speed, Frequency and Wavelength are Linked by the Wave Equation

Wave speed can be measured just like the speed of anything else:

$$\text{Speed } (v) = \frac{\text{distance moved } (d)}{\text{time taken } (t)}$$

Remember, you're not measuring how fast a physical point (like one molecule of rope) moves. You're measuring how fast a point on the **wave pattern** moves.

Learn the **Wave Equation**...

Speed of wave (***v***) = wavelength (**λ**) × frequency (***f***)

$$v = \lambda f$$

You need to be able to rearrange this equation for v, λ or f.

... and How to **Derive** it

You can work out the **wave equation** by imagining **how long** it takes for the **crest** of a wave to **move** across a **distance** of **one wavelength**. The **distance travelled** is λ. **By definition**, the **time taken** to travel **one whole wavelength** is the **period** of the wave, which is equal to **1/*f***.

$$\text{Speed } (v) = \frac{\text{distance moved } (d)}{\text{time taken } (t)} \longrightarrow \text{Speed } (v) = \frac{\text{distance moved } (\lambda)}{\text{time taken } (1/f)}$$

Learn to recognise when to use ***v*** = **λ*f*** and when to use ***v*** = ***d/t***. Look at which variables are mentioned in the question.

Practice Questions

Q1 Does a wave carry matter **or** energy from one place to another?

Q2 Diffraction and interference are two wave properties. Write down two more.

Q3 Write down the relationship between the frequency of a wave and its time period.

Q4 Give the units of frequency, displacement and amplitude.

Q5 Write down the equation connecting ***v***, **λ** and ***f***.

Exam Question

Q1 A buoy floating on the sea takes 6 seconds to rise and fall once (complete a full period of oscillation). The difference in height between the buoy at its lowest and highest points is 1.2 m, and waves pass it at a speed of 3 ms^{-1}.

(a) The wavelength of the waves is **A** 14 m **B** 16 m **C** 18 m **D** 20 m [1 mark]

(b) The amplitude of the waves is **A** 1.2 m **B** 2.4 m **C** 0.6 m **D** 0.12 m [1 mark]

Learn the wave equation and its derivation — pure poetry...

This isn't too difficult to start you off — most of it you'll have done at GCSE anyway. But once again, it's a whole bunch of equations to learn, and you won't get far without learning them. Yada yada.

Longitudinal and Transverse Waves

There are different types of wave — and the difference is easiest to see using a slinky. Try it — you'll have hours of fun.

In Transverse Waves *the* Vibration *is at* Right Angles *to the* Direction *of Travel*

All **electromagnetic waves** are **transverse**. Other examples of transverse waves are **ripples** on water and waves on **ropes**.

There are **two** main ways of **drawing** transverse waves:

1) They can be shown as **graphs of displacement against distance along the path of the wave.**

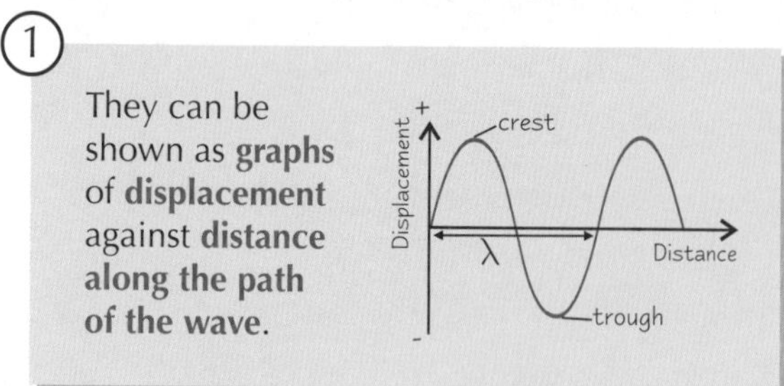

2) Or, they can be shown as graphs of **displacement against time** for a point as the wave passes.

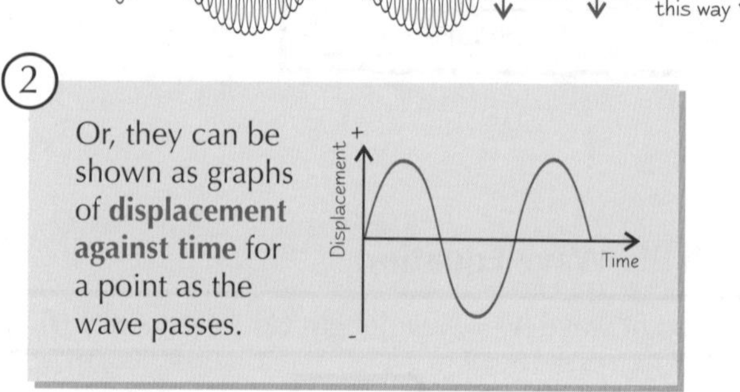

Both sorts of graph often give the **same shape**, so make sure you check out the label on the **x-axis**. Displacements **upwards** from the centre line are given a **+ sign**. Displacements downwards are given a **– sign**.

In Longitudinal Waves *the* Vibrations *are* Along *the Direction of Travel*

The most **common** example of a **longitudinal wave** is **sound**. A sound wave consists of alternate **compressions** and **rarefactions** of the **medium** it's travelling through. (That's why sound can't go through a vacuum.) Some types of **earthquake shock waves** are also longitudinal.

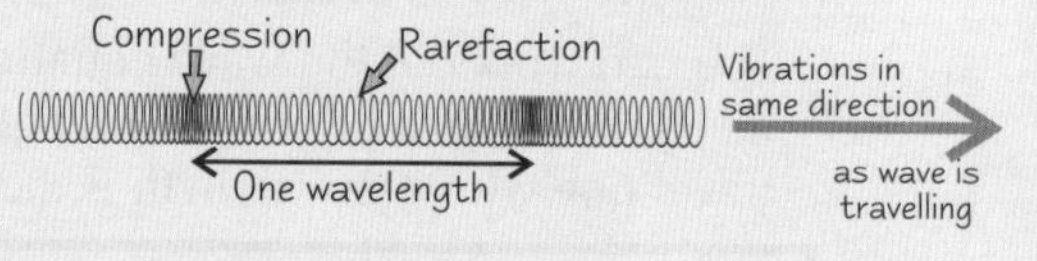

It's hard to **represent** longitudinal waves **graphically**. You'll usually see them plotted as **displacement** against **time**. These can be **confusing** though, because they look like a **transverse wave**.

A Polarised Wave *only* Oscillates *In One Direction*

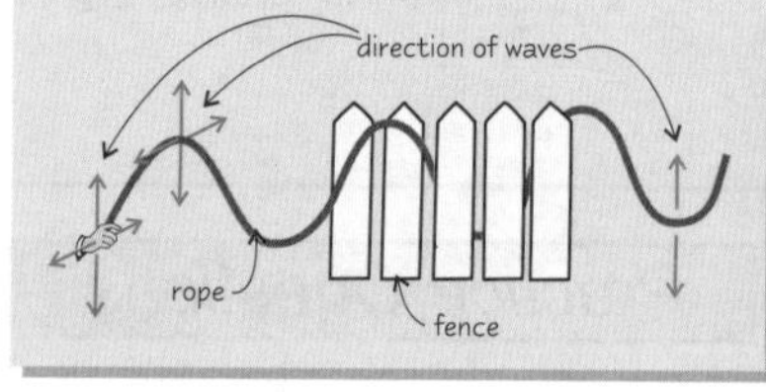

1) If you **shake a rope** to make a **wave** you can move your hand **up and down** or **side to side** or in a **mixture** of directions — it still makes a **transverse wave**.
2) But if you try to pass **waves in a rope** through a **vertical fence**, the wave will only get through if the **vibrations** are **vertical**. The fence filters out vibration in other directions. This is called **polarising** the wave.
3) Ordinary **light waves** are a mixture of **different directions** of **vibration**. (The things vibrating are electric and magnetic fields.) A **polarising filter** only transmits vibrations in one direction.
4) If you have two polarising filters at **right angles** to each other, then **no** light will get through.
5) Polarisation **can only happen** for **transverse** waves. The fact that you can polarise light is one **proof** that it's a transverse wave.

When Light Reflects *it is* Partially Polarised

1) Rotating a **polarising filter** in a beam of light shows the fraction of the light that is vibrating in each **direction**.
2) If you direct a beam of unpolarised light at a reflective surface then view the **reflected ray** through a polarising filter, the intensity of light leaving the filter **changes** with the **orientation** of the filter.
3) The intensity changes because light is **partially polarised** when it is **reflected**.
4) This effect is used to remove **unwanted reflections** in photography and in **Polaroid sunglasses** to remove **glare**.

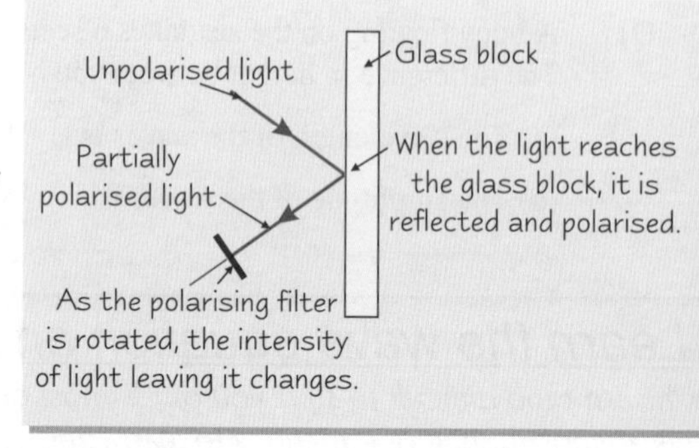

Longitudinal and Transverse Waves

Television** and **Radio Signals** are **Polarised

If you walk down the street and look up at the **TV aerials** on people's houses, you'll see that the **rods** (the sticky-out bits) on them are all **horizontal**. The reason for this is that **TV signals** are **polarised** by the orientation of the **rods** on the **broadcasting aerial**.
To receive a strong signal, you have to **line up** the **rods** on the **receiving aerial** with the **rods** on the **transmitting aerial** — if they aren't aligned, the signal strength will be lower.

It's the **same** with **radio** — if you try **tuning a radio** and then **moving** the **aerial** around, your signal will **come and go** as the transmitting and receiving aerials go in and out of **alignment**.

The rods on this broadcasting aerial are horizontal.

*Materials Can **Rotate** the **Plane of Polarisation***

The **plane** in which a wave moves and **vibrates** is called the **plane of polarisation** — e.g. the rope on the last page was polarised in the **vertical** plane by the fence. Some **materials** (e.g. crystals) **rotate** the plane of polarised light. You can **measure** how much a material rotates the plane of polarised light using two **polarising filters**:

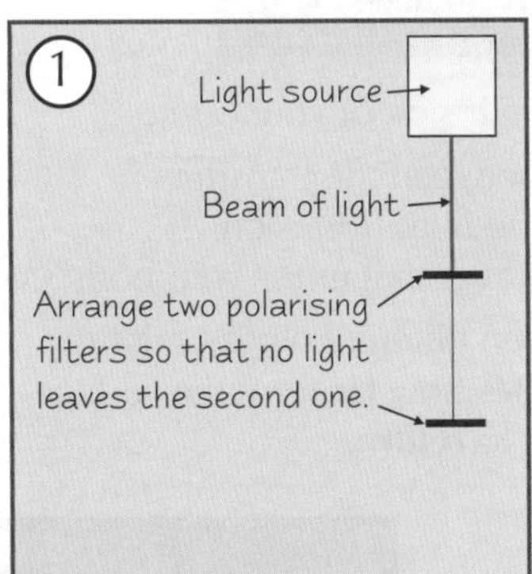

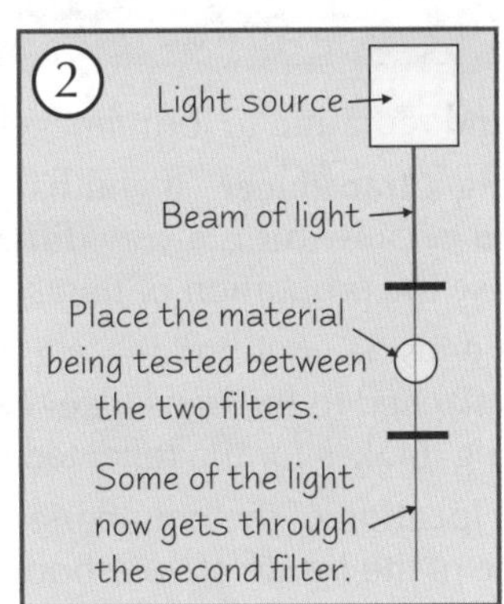

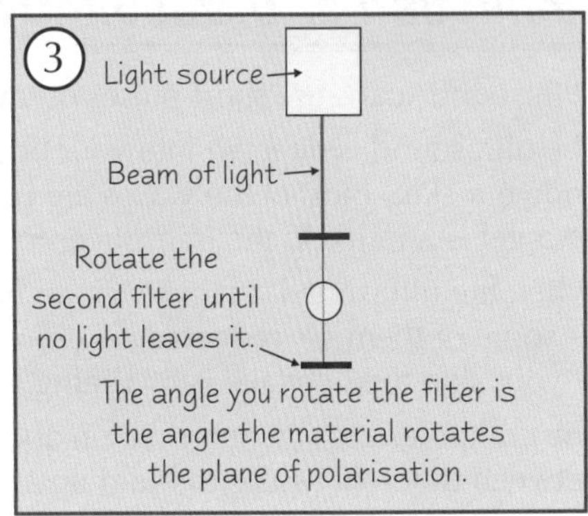

Practice Questions

Q1 Give examples of a transverse wave and a longitudinal wave.

Q2 What is a polarised wave?

Q3 How can you polarise a wave?

Q4 Why do you have to line up transmitting and receiving television aerials?

Exam Questions

Q1 In an experiment, light is shone through a disc of a crystal called "Iceland spar". The beam of light is less bright when it emerges from the crystal than when it enters. Next, a second identical disc of Iceland spar is placed in front of the first. The first disc is held steady while the second is rotated (in the plane of the disc). The intensity of light emerging changes as the second disc rotates. At two points in each rotation, no light gets through at all.

Explain the results of these experiments. You may use a diagram to help your answer. [5 marks]

Q2 Give one example of an application of polarisation and explain how it works. [2 marks]

Caution — rotating the plane may cause nausea...

Right, there's lots to learn on these two pages so I won't hold you up with chat. Don't panic though — a lot of this stuff will be familiar from GCSE, so it's not like you're starting from scratch. One last thing — I know television is on this page, but it doesn't mean you can tune in and call it revision — it won't help. A nice cup of tea, on the other hand, always helps.

Ultrasound Imaging

Now that you've seen how waves work, it's time to see what they're used for — scanning, that's what.

Waves are Reflected and Transmitted at Interfaces

1) The **boundary** between two different media is called an **interface**.
2) When a wave passes from one medium to another, some of its **energy** is **reflected** and some of it is **transmitted** — as shown in the diagram.
3) The proportion of energy reflected or transmitted depends on the two media involved. If the media are very **different**, most of the energy is **reflected**. If they are quite **similar**, most of the energy is **transmitted**.
4) For **light**, the proportion of the wave reflected and transmitted depends on the **refractive index** of the two materials (see page 46).

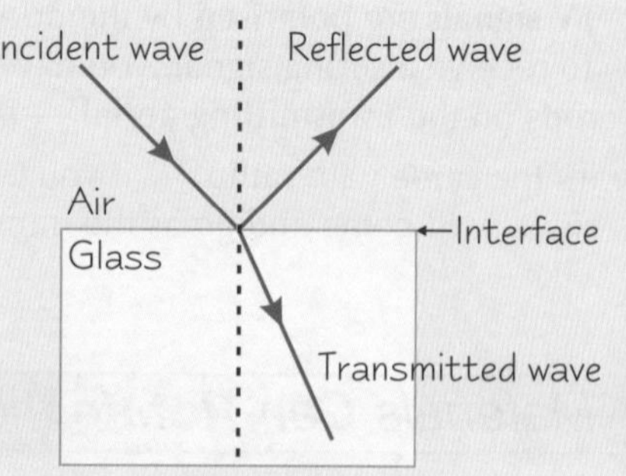

The Reflection of Ultrasound Waves is Used in Ultrasound Scans

1) Ultrasound scans use short pulses of **ultrasound radiation** to form images of the inside of your body.
2) The ultrasound is directed into your body using a **transducer**. If you have air between the transducer and your skin, most of the waves are **reflected** because air is a very **different** medium from skin. So a **gel** is applied to the transducer to **increase** the proportion of ultrasound waves that **enter** your body.
3) When the ultrasound waves reach an **interface** inside your body — e.g. between different types of tissue — some of them are **reflected**. A computer attached to the transducer calculates how far from the surface of your skin the interface is by **timing** how long it takes for the reflected waves to **return**.
4) The computer uses the information about the **location** of the boundaries between different tissues to build up an **image** of the inside of your body.

A similar technique is used in **sonar** — e.g. ships send sonar pulses (**ultrasound waves**) down towards the seabed and the pulses are **reflected** back from any **submerged** objects. It can also be used to measure the **speed** of objects.

You Can Measure the Speed of Objects Using the Doppler Effect

1) If you stand **still** and listen to the sound of the horn of a **stationary** car, you'll hear the **same pitch** sound no matter where you stand.
2) But if the car is **moving** when it sounds its horn, the pitch you hear will be **different** — it'll be **lower** if the car is moving **away** from you and **higher** if it's moving **towards** you. This is the **Doppler effect**.
3) When the car is moving **away** from you, the sound waves travel in the **opposite** direction from the car, so are **stretched** out — i.e. have a **longer wavelength** and **lower frequency** when they reach you.
4) The opposite happens when the car is moving **towards** you — the sound waves **bunch up**, so have a **shorter wavelength** and **higher frequency** when they get to you.

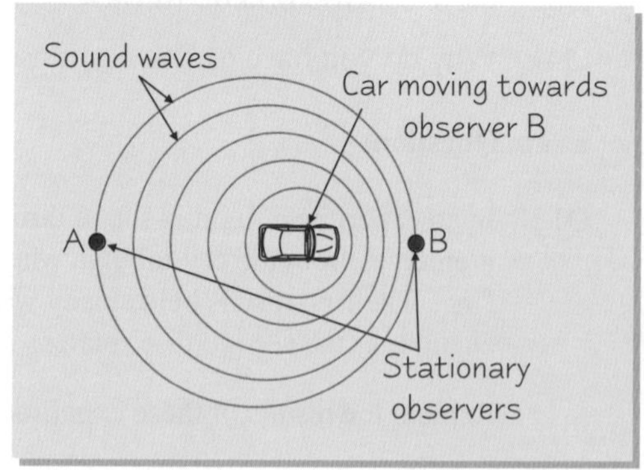

Not all police forces use radar guns to catch speeding motorists.

5) How much the sound waves change depends on how **fast** the car is travelling — the **greater** the car's **speed**, the **larger** the **change**. This means the Doppler effect can be used to **measure the speed** of moving objects.
6) The Doppler effect happens with **all waves**, so it has a wide range of applications. For example, **police radar guns** measure the speed of cars using **microwaves**, while **ultrasound sonography** is used to monitor the function of **blood vessels** by measuring how fast **blood** is flowing inside them.

Ultrasound Imaging

Shorter Wavelengths Produce *Clearer Images*

Ultrasound scanning can be a really useful technique — but only if the images are **clear**.
The **properties** of the ultrasound **radiation** used has a big effect on the clarity of the images produced.

1) **Shorter** wavelengths **diffract** (see page 52) much **less** than longer wavelengths.
2) This means that the shorter the **wavelength** of the ultrasound, the less the waves **spread out** as they travel and the more **precisely** the location of the interfaces between tissues can be mapped.
3) So ultrasound scanners use waves with a **high frequency** and **short wavelength**.

Shorter Pulses Produce *Clearer Images*

Ultrasound transducers cannot **transmit** and **receive** pulses at the same time. If **reflected** waves reach the transducer while it is **transmitting**, the information they contain will be **lost** and image **quality** will be reduced. This means:

1) The **pulses** of ultrasound transmitted must be **very short** (a few microseconds long) so that the reflections from nearby interfaces don't reach the transducer before the pulse has ended.
2) The gap between pulses must be **long** (at least 1 millisecond) so that all the reflected waves from one pulse return to the transducer **before** the next pulse is transmitted.

Developments in *Science* and *Technology* Have *Social* and *Ethical Issues*

When scientists work, they have to consider whether what they want to achieve is possible and whether it **should** be done at all. For example, when deciding whether a **medical technique** should be used, scientists consider:

1) **Safety** — will the technique cause more **harm** than **good**? For example, an **X-ray** might show up a problem that an ultrasound scan cannot, but X-rays are known to **damage cells** whereas ultrasound is not (so far).
2) **Social issues** — will the technique **benefit society** or adversely affect people? For example, ultrasound scans of **unborn foetuses** allow doctors to spot problems or abnormal growth, giving them a chance to **put it right**.
3) **Ethical issues** — is the technique **morally right**? Will it lead to dangerous new developments? For example, ultrasound scans can be used to show the **gender** of foetuses, but this might lead to **unnecessary** terminations.
4) **Cost** — do the **benefits** of the technique outweigh the **expense**? For example, **MRI scanning** is less dangerous than **X-ray imaging** and gives clearer pictures than ultrasound, but is much more **expensive** than either.

Practice Questions

Q1 What is an interface? What happens to a wave when it reaches an interface?

Q2 How is sonar similar to ultrasound scanning?

Q3 State and explain two things you can do to improve the clarity of an ultrasound image.

Exam Questions

Q1 Ultrasound scans can be used to measure the rate of blood flow within a person's body. The diagram shows the ultrasound wave transmitted into a patient.

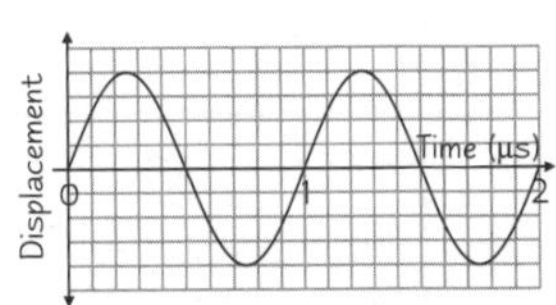

(a) Sketch the ultrasound wave reflected from blood flowing towards the receiver. [1 mark]

(b) Sketch the ultrasound wave reflected from blood flowing away from the receiver. [1 mark]

Q2 Describe and explain two social/ethical issues concerning a planned space mission to Mars. [4 marks]

I've got social issues — no one likes me...

An interesting fact for you — Christian Doppler (of Doppler effect fame) lived practically next door to Mozart. Except that Mozart travelled all around the world and died before Doppler was born, but they're just minor details.

The Electromagnetic Spectrum

There's nothing really deep and meaningful to understand on this page — just a load of facts to learn I'm afraid.

All **Electromagnetic Waves** Have Some **Properties** In Common

1) They travel in a **vacuum** at a **speed** of **2.998 × 10⁸ ms⁻¹**, and at slower speeds in other media.
2) They are **transverse** waves consisting of **vibrating electric** and **magnetic fields.** The **electric** and **magnetic** fields are at **right angles** to each other and to the **direction of travel.**
3) Like all waves, EM waves can be **reflected**, **refracted** and **diffracted** and can undergo **interference**.
4) Like all waves, EM waves obey $v = f\lambda$ (v = velocity, f = frequency, λ = wavelength).
5) Like all progressive waves, progressive EM waves **carry energy**.
6) Like all transverse waves, EM waves can be **polarised.**

Some **Properties Vary** Across the **EM Spectrum**

EM waves with different wavelengths behave differently in some respects. The spectrum is split into seven categories: **radio waves**, **microwaves**, **infrared**, **visible light**, **ultraviolet**, **X-rays** and **gamma rays**.

1) The longer the wavelength, the more **obvious** the wave characteristics — e.g., long radio waves diffract round hills.
2) **Energy** is directly proportional to **frequency**. **Gamma rays** have the **highest energy**; **radio waves** the **lowest**.
3) The **higher** the **energy**, in general the more **dangerous** the wave.
4) The **lower the energy** of an EM wave, the **further from the nucleus** it comes from. **Gamma radiation** comes from inside the **nucleus**. **X-rays to visible light** come from energy-level transitions in **atoms** (see p. 71). **Infrared** radiation and **microwaves** are associated with **molecules**. **Radio waves** come from oscillations in **electric fields**.

The **Properties** of an **EM Wave** Change with **Wavelength**

Type	Approximate wavelength / m	Penetration	Uses
Radio waves	10^{-1} — 10^{6}	Pass through matter.	Radio transmissions.
Microwaves	10^{-3} — 10^{-1}	Mostly pass through matter, but cause some heating.	Radar. Microwave cookery. TV transmissions.
Infrared (IR)	7×10^{-7} — 10^{-3}	Mostly absorbed by matter, causing it to heat up.	Heat detectors. Night-vision cameras. Remote controls. Optical fibres.
Visible light	4×10^{-7} — 7×10^{-7}	Absorbed by matter, causing some heating effect.	Human sight. Optical fibres.
Ultraviolet (UV)	10^{-8} — 4×10^{-7}	Absorbed by matter. Slight ionisation.	Sunbeds. Security markings that show up in UV light.
X-rays	10^{-13} — 10^{-8}	Mostly pass through matter, but cause ionisation as they pass.	To see damage to bones and teeth. Airport security scanners. To kill cancer cells.
Gamma rays	10^{-16} — 10^{-10}	Mostly pass through matter, but cause ionisation as they pass.	Irradiation of food. Sterilisation of medical instruments. To kill cancer cells.

The Electromagnetic Spectrum

Different Types of EM Wave Have Different **Effects** on the **Body**

Type	Production	Effect on human body
Radio waves	Oscillating electrons in an aerial	No effect.
Microwaves	Electron tube oscillators. Masers.	Absorbed by water — danger of cooking human body*.
Infrared (IR)	Natural and artificial heat sources.	Heating. Excess heat can harm the body's systems.
Visible light	Natural and artificial light sources.	Used for sight. Too bright a light can damage eyes.
Ultraviolet (UV)	e.g. the Sun.	Tans the skin. Can cause skin cancer and eye damage.
X-rays	Bombarding metal with electrons.	Cancer due to cell damage. Eye damage.
Gamma rays	Radioactive decay of the nucleus.	Cancer due to cell damage. Eye damage.

1) UV radiation is split into categories based on frequency — **UV-A**, **UV-B** and **UV-C**.
2) **UV-A** is the **least damaging**, although it's thought to be a major cause of **skin aging**.
3) **UV-B** is more dangerous — it's responsible for **sunburn** and can lead to **cancer** too.
4) **UV-C** is **ionising** — it can cause **cell mutation** or **destruction**, and **cancer**. It's almost **entirely blocked** by the ozone layer, though.
5) **Dark** skin gives some protection from UV rays, stopping them reaching more vulnerable tissues below — so **tanning** is a protection mechanism.
6) **Sunscreens** provide some protection from UV in sunlight. They're designed to **limit** the amount of **UV-A** and **UV-B** radiation reaching your skin.

* Or small animals.

Practice Questions

Q1 What are the main practical uses of infrared radiation?

Q2 Which types of electromagnetic radiation have the highest and lowest energies?

Q3 What is the significance of the speed 2.998×10^8 ms^{-1}?

Q4 Why are microwaves dangerous?

Q5 How does the energy of an EM wave vary with frequency?

Exam Questions

Q1 In a vacuum, do X-rays travel faster, slower or at the same speed as visible light? Explain your answer. [2 marks]

Q2 (a) Describe briefly the physics behind a practical use of X rays. [2 marks]

(b) What is the difference between gamma rays and X-rays? [2 marks]

Q3 Give an example of a type of electromagnetic wave causing a hazard to health. [2 marks]

I've got UV hair...

No really I have. It's great. It's purple. And it's got shiny glittery white bits in it. Aaaanyway... moving swiftly on. Loads of facts to learn on these pages. You probably know most of this from GCSE anyway, but make sure you know it well enough to answer a question on it in the exam. Not much fun, but... there you go.

Refractive Index

The stuff on the next two pages explains why your legs look short in a swimming pool.

The Refractive Index of a Material Measures How Much It Slows Down Light

Light goes fastest in a **vacuum**. It **slows down** in other materials, because it **interacts** with the particles in them. The more **optically dense** a material is, the more light slows down when it enters it.

The **absolute refractive index** of a material, μ, is the **ratio** between the **speed of light** in a **vacuum**, c, and the speed of light in that **material**, v.

$$\mu = \frac{c}{v}$$

$c = 3 \times 10^8\ \text{ms}^{-1}$

The **relative** refractive index **between two materials**, ${}_1\mu_2$, is the ratio of the speed of light **in material 1** to the speed of light **in material 2**.

$${}_1\mu_2 = \frac{v_1}{v_2}$$

Combining the two equations gives:

$${}_1\mu_2 = \frac{\mu_2}{\mu_1}$$

The speed of light in air is only a tiny bit smaller than c. So you can assume the refractive index of air is 1.

1) The **absolute refractive index** of a material is a **property** of that material only. But a **relative refractive index** is a property of the **interface** between two materials. It's different for **every possible pair**.
2) Because you can assume $\mu_{air} = 1$, you can assume the refractive index for an **air to glass boundary** equals the **absolute refractive index** of the glass.

Snell's Law uses Angles to Calculate the Refractive Index

1) The **angle** the **incoming light** makes to the **normal** is called the **angle of incidence**, ***i***. The **angle** the **refracted ray** makes with the **normal** is the **angle of refraction**, ***r***.
2) When light enters an optically denser medium it is refracted **towards** the normal.
3) μ, ***i*** and ***r*** are related by **Snell's law**.

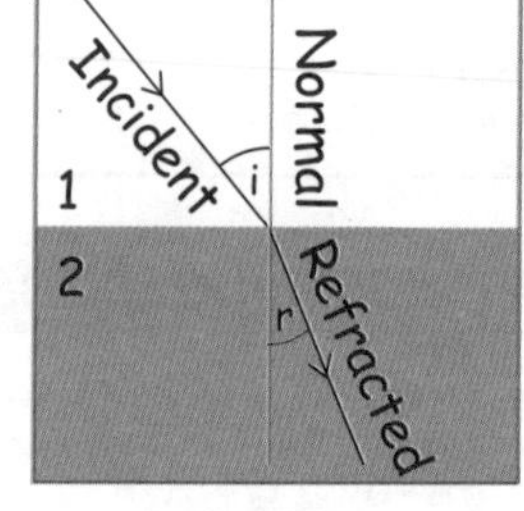

$$\mu_1 \sin i = \mu_2 \sin r$$

You don't need to know the geometry of why Snell's law works, but you need to be able to use it.

4) You can use a device called a **refractometer** to accurately measure the refractive index of a material. The machine shines a beam of light at the sample. You then view the refracted beam through a **microscope** and measure its angle of refraction.

Sometimes You Need to Know Refractive Index **Very Accurately**

1) **Making lenses** — There are several different types of glass that can be used to make lenses, and they all have different refractive indices. The refractive index of the glass affects how thick and how curved the lens has to be to get the same magnifying power.
It's important to know the refractive index accurately so you can calculate the exact shape of lens to fit, say, someone's prescription for a pair of glasses.
2) **In forensic investigations** — Identifying broken bits of glass and plastic can be vital when tracking down crime suspects. Once you know the exact refractive index of the glass from the crime scene, you can compare it with shards found on the clothes or shoes of a suspect. Most shards are too small for a refractometer, so you need to measure the refractive index differently. You use the fact that if two materials with the same refractive index are side by side, you can't see the boundary between them.

Refractive Index

Light Leaving an **Optically Denser Material** is Refracted **Away** from the **Normal**

When light **goes from** an optically denser material into an optically **less dense** material (e.g. glass to air), interesting things can start to happen.

Shine a ray of light at a **glass to air** boundary, then gradually **increase** the angle of incidence. As you increase the angle of incidence, the angle of **refraction** gets closer and closer to **90°**. Eventually i reaches a **critical angle** C for which $r = 90°$. The light is **refracted** along the **boundary**.

At this **critical angle**, Snell's law $\mu_{glass} \sin i = \mu_{air} \sin r$ becomes:

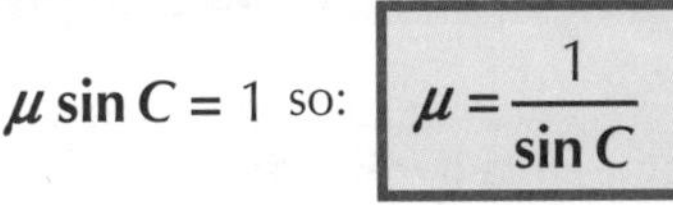

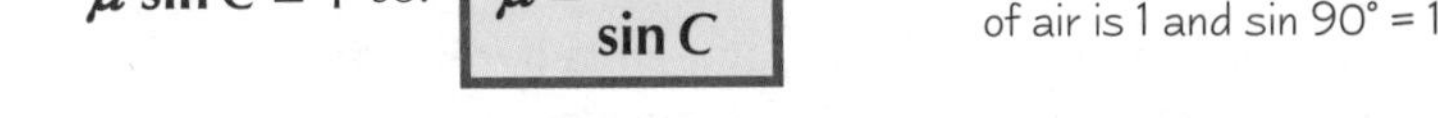

$\mu \sin C = 1$ so: $$\mu = \frac{1}{\sin C}$$

That's because the refractive index of air is 1 and sin 90° = 1

At angles of incidence **greater than** C refraction is **impossible**.
That means **all** the light is reflected back into the material. This effect is called **total internal reflection**.

Optical Fibres Use Total Internal Reflection

1) An optical fibre is a very **thin flexible tube** of **glass** or **plastic** fibre that can carry **light signals** over long distances and round corners.
2) The optical fibres themselves have a **high refractive index** but are surrounded by **cladding** with a lower refractive index.
3) Light is shone in at **one end** of the fibre. The fibre is so **narrow** that the light always **hits the boundary** between fibre and cladding at an **angle bigger** than the **critical angle**.
4) So all the light is **totally internally reflected** from boundary to boundary until it reaches the other end.

Light running through optical fibres is used to transmit **phone and cable TV signals**.
It beats the **old system** of using **electricity** flowing through **copper cables**:

1) The signal can carry **more information** because visible light has a high frequency.
2) The light **doesn't heat up the fibre** — so almost no energy is lost as heat.
3) There is no electrical **interference**.

Practice Questions

Q1 Why does light go fastest in a vacuum and slow down in other media?

Q2 What is the formula for the critical angle for a ray of light at a water/air boundary?

Exam Questions

Q1 (a) Light travels in diamond at 1.24×10^8 ms^{-1}. What is the refractive index of diamond? [1 mark]

(b) What is the angle of refraction if light strikes a facet of a diamond ring at an angle of 50° to the normal of the air/diamond boundary? [2 marks]

Q2 An adjustable underwater spotlight is placed on the floor of an aquarium tank. When the light points upwards at a steep angle a beam comes through the surface of the water into the air, and the tank is dimly lit. When the spotlight is placed at a shallower angle, no light comes up through the water surface, and the tank is brightly lit.

(a) Explain what is happening. [2 marks]

(b) It is found that the beam into the air disappears when the spotlight is pointed at any angle of less than 41.25° to the floor. Calculate the refractive index of water. [2 marks]

I don't care about expensive things — all I care about is wave speed...

AS Physics examiners are always saying how candidates do worst in the waves bit of the exam. You'd think they'd have something more important to worry about — third world poverty, war, Posh & Becks... But no.

Superposition and Coherence

When two waves get together, it can be either really impressive or really disappointing.

Superposition Happens When **Two** or **More** Waves **Pass Through** Each Other

1) At the **instant** the waves **cross**, the **displacements** due to each wave **combine**. Then **each wave** goes on its merry way. You can **see** this if **two pulses** are sent **simultaneously** from each end of a rope.
2) The **principle of superposition** says that when two or more **waves cross**, the **resultant** displacement equals the **vector sum** of the **individual** displacements.

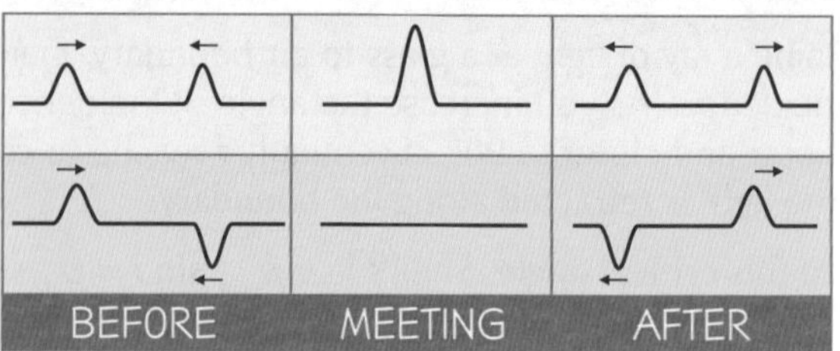

"Superposition" means "one thing on top of another thing". You can use the same idea in reverse — a complex wave can be separated out mathematically into several simple sine waves of various sizes.

Interference can be **Constructive** or **Destructive**

1) A **crest** plus a **crest** gives a **big crest**. A **trough** plus a **trough** gives a **big trough**. These are both examples of **constructive interference**.
2) A **crest** plus a **trough** of **equal size** gives... **nothing**. The two displacements **cancel each other out** completely. This is called **destructive interference**.
3) If the **crest** and the **trough** aren't the **same size**, then the destructive interference **isn't total**. For the interference to be **noticeable**, the two **amplitudes** should be **nearly equal**.

Graphically, you can superimpose waves by adding the individual displacements at each point along the *x*-axis, and then plotting them.

In **Phase** Means In **Step** — Two Points **In Phase** Interfere **Constructively**

1) Two points on a wave are **in phase** if they are both at the **same point** in the **wave cycle**. Points in phase have the **same displacement** and **velocity**.
   On the graph, points **A** and **B** are **in phase**; points **A** and **C** are **out of phase**.

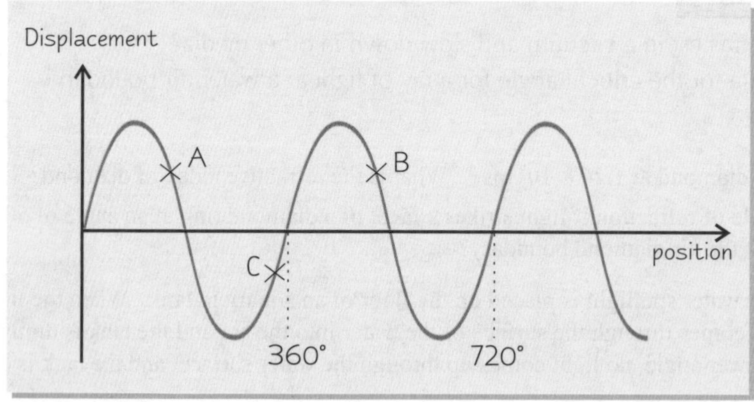

2) It's mathematically **handy** to show one **complete cycle** of a wave as an **angle of 360° (2π radians)**.
   Two points with a **phase difference** of **zero** or a **multiple of 360°** are **in phase**.
   Points with a **phase difference** of **odd-number multiples** of **180° (π radians)** are **exactly out of phase**.
3) You can also talk about two **different waves** being **in phase**. **In practice** this happens because **both** waves came from the **same oscillator**. In **other** situations there will nearly always be a **phase difference** between two waves.

Superposition and Coherence

To Get Interference Patterns the Two Sources Must Be Coherent

Interference **still happens** when you're observing waves of **different wavelength** and **frequency** — but it happens in a **jumble**. In order to get clear **interference patterns**, the two or more sources must be **coherent**.

Two sources are **coherent** if they have the **same wavelength** and **frequency** and a **fixed phase difference** between them.

In exam questions at AS, the 'fixed phase difference' is almost certainly going to be zero. The two sources will be in phase.

Constructive or Destructive Interference Depends on the Path Difference

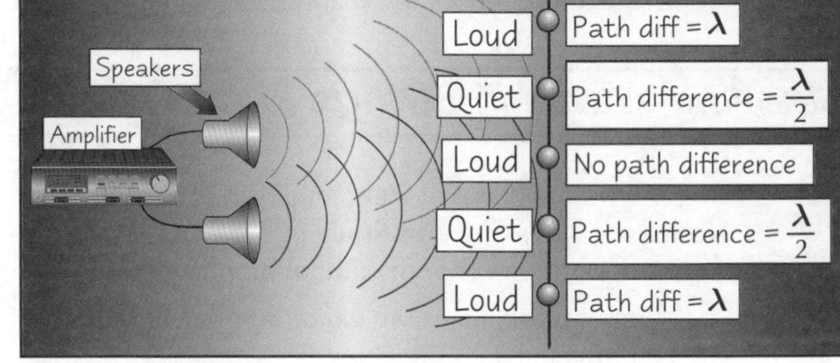

1) Whether you get **constructive** or **destructive** interference at a **point** depends on how **much further one wave** has travelled than the **other wave** to get to that point.
2) The **amount** by which the path travelled by one wave is **longer** than the path travelled by the other wave is called the **path difference.**
3) At **any point an equal distance** from both sources you will get **constructive interference.** You also get constructive interference at any point where the **path difference** is a **whole number of wavelengths**. At these points the two waves are **in phase** and **reinforce** each other. But at points where the path difference is **half a wavelength**, **one and a half** wavelengths, **two and a half** wavelengths etc., the waves arrive **out of phase** and you get **destructive interference**.

Constructive interference occurs when: path difference $= n\lambda$ (where n is an integer)

Destructive interference occurs when: path difference $= \frac{(2n + 1)\lambda}{2} = (n + \frac{1}{2})\lambda$

Practice Questions

Q1 Why does the principle of superposition deal with the **vector** sum of two displacements?

Q2 What happens when a crest meets a slightly smaller trough?

Q3 If two points on a wave have a phase difference of 1440°, are they in phase?

Exam Questions

Q1 (a) Two sources are coherent.
What can you say about their frequencies, wavelengths and phase difference? [2 marks]

(b) Suggest why you might have difficulty in observing interference patterns in an area affected by two waves from two sources even though the two sources are coherent. [1 mark]

Q2 Two points on an undamped wave are exactly out of phase.

(a) What is the phase difference between them, expressed in degrees? [1 mark]

(b) Compare the displacements and velocities of the two points. [2 marks]

Learn this and you'll be in a super position to pass your exam...

...I'll get my coat.

There are a few really crucial concepts here: a) interference can be constructive or destructive, b) constructive interference happens when the path difference is a whole number of wavelengths, c) the sources must be coherent.

Standing (Stationary) Waves

Standing waves are waves that... er... stand still... well, not still exactly... I mean, well...they don't go anywhere... um...

You get Standing Waves When a **Progressive Wave** is **Reflected** at a **Boundary**

A standing wave is the **superposition** of **two progressive waves** with the **same wavelength**, moving in **opposite directions**.

1) Unlike progressive waves, **no energy** is transmitted by a standing wave.
2) You can demonstrate standing waves by setting up a **driving oscillator** at one end of a **stretched string** with the other end fixed. The wave generated by the oscillator is **reflected** back and forth.
3) For most frequencies the resultant **pattern** is a **jumble**. However, if the oscillator happens to produce an **exact number of waves** in the time it takes for a wave to get to the **end** and **back again**, then the **original** and **reflected** waves **reinforce** each other.
4) At these **"resonant frequencies"** you get a **standing wave** where the **pattern doesn't move** — it just sits there, bobbing up and down. Happy, at peace with the world...

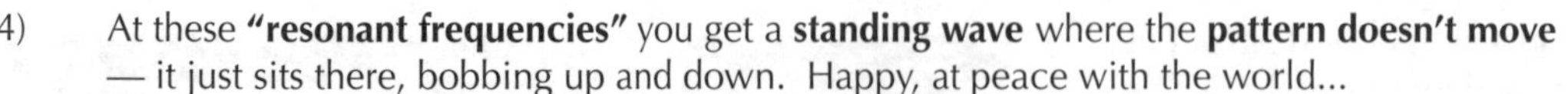

A sitting wave.

Standing Waves in **Strings** Form **Oscillating "Loops"** Separated by **Nodes**

1) Each particle vibrates at **right angles** to the string. **Nodes** are where the **amplitude** of the vibration is **zero**. **Antinodes** are points of **maximum amplitude**.
2) At resonant frequencies, an **exact number** of **half wavelengths** fits onto the string.

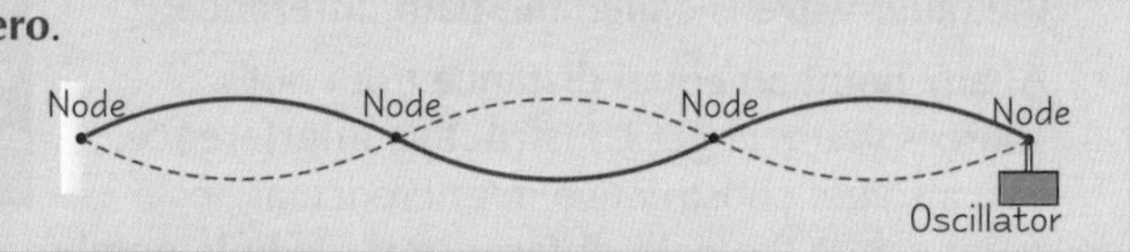

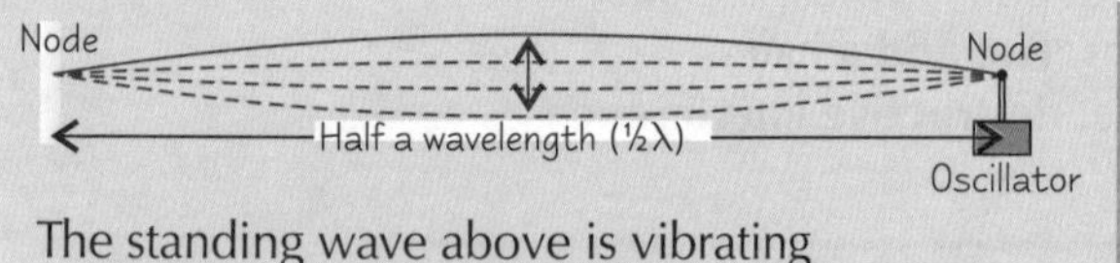

The standing wave above is vibrating at the **lowest possible** resonant frequency (the **fundamental frequency**). It has **one "loop"** with a **node at each end**.

This is the **second harmonic** (or **first overtone**). It is **twice** the fundamental frequency. There are two **"loops"** with a **node** in the **middle** and **one at each end**.

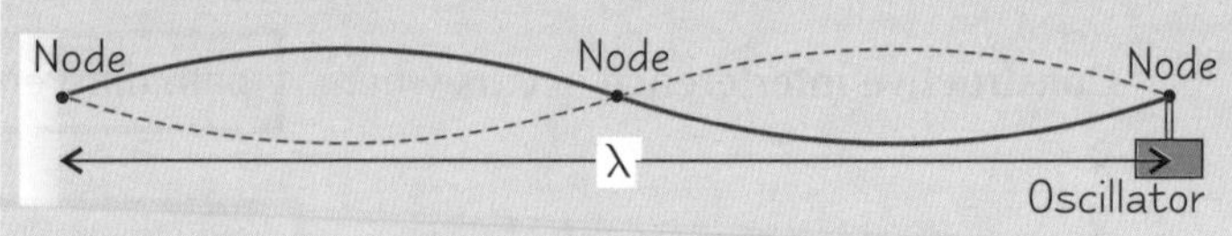

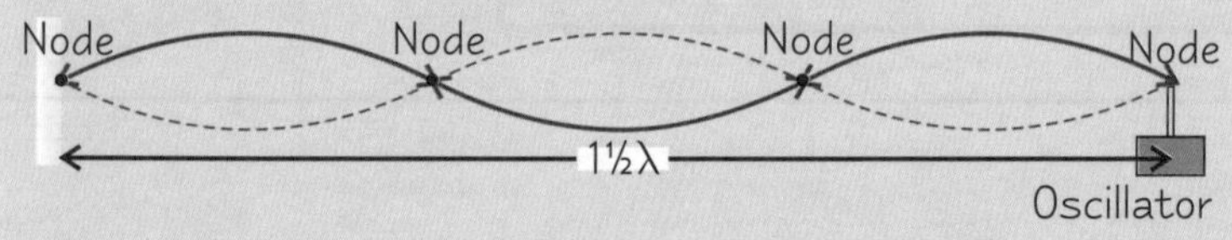

The **third harmonic** (or **second overtone**) is **three times** the fundamental frequency. **1½ wavelengths** fit on the string.

The **Notes** Played by **Stringed** and **Wind Instruments** Are Standing Waves

Transverse standing waves form on the strings of **stringed instruments** like **violins** and **guitars**. Your finger or the bow sets the **string vibrating** at the point of contact. Waves are sent out in **both directions** and **reflected** back at both ends.

Longitudinal Standing Waves Form in a **Wind Instrument** or Other **Air Column**

1) If a source of sound is placed at the open end of a flute, piccolo, oboe or other column of air, there will be some **frequencies** for which **resonance** occurs and a standing wave is set up.
2) If the instrument has a **closed end**, a **node** will form there. You get the lowest resonant frequency when the length of the pipe is a **quarter wavelength**.

$$l = \frac{\lambda}{4}$$

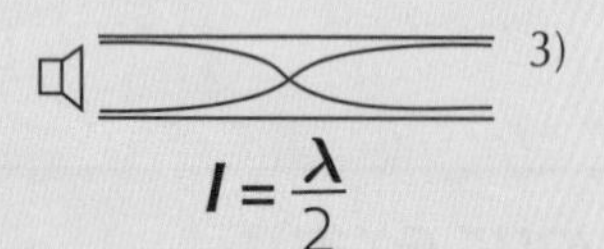

$$l = \frac{\lambda}{2}$$

3) **Antinodes** form at the **open ends** of pipes. If both ends are open, you get the lowest resonant frequency when the length of the pipe is a **half wavelength**.

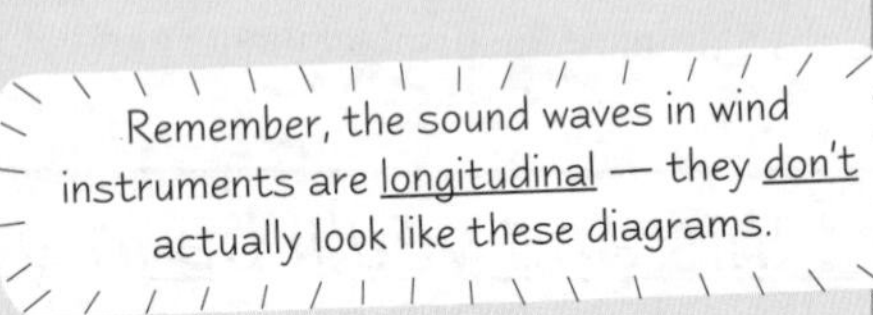

Standing (Stationary) Waves

*You can **Demonstrate Standing Waves** with Microwaves and Sounds*

Microwaves Reflected Off a Metal Plate Set Up a Standing Wave

Microwave standing wave apparatus ⟶

You can find the **nodes** and **antinodes** by moving the **probe** between **transmitter** and **reflecting** plate.

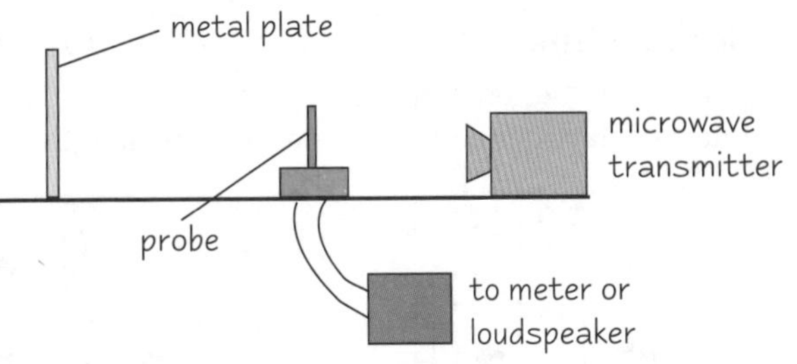

Powder can Show Standing Waves in a Tube of Air

Stationary sound waves are produced in the **glass tube**. The **lycopodium powder** (don't worry, you don't need to know what that is) laid along the bottom of the tube is **shaken away** from the **antinodes** but left **undisturbed** at the **nodes**.

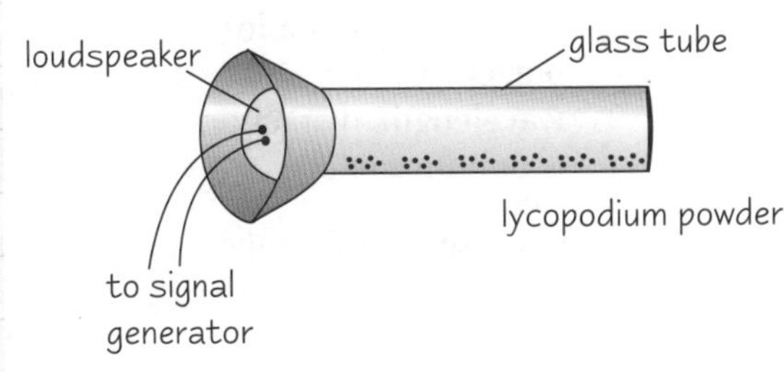

Practice Questions

Q1 How do standing waves form?

Q2 At four times the fundamental frequency, how many half wavelengths fit on a violin string?

Q3 Describe an experiment to investigate standing waves in a column of air.

Exam Question

Q1 (a) A standing wave of three times the fundamental frequency is formed on a stretched string of length 1.2m. Sketch a diagram showing the form of the wave. [2 marks]

(b) What is the wavelength of the standing wave? [1 mark]

(c) Explain how the amplitude varies along the string. How is that different from the amplitude of a progressive wave? [2 marks]

(d) At a given moment, how does the displacement of a particle at one antinode compare to the displacement of a particle at the next antinode? [2 marks]

Just get hold of a guitar and try it out...

Exam questions often get you to compare standing waves to progressive waves.
Remember the fundamental (ho ho) difference is that standing waves don't transmit energy.

Diffraction

Ripple tanks, ripple tanks — yeah.

*Waves Go **Round Corners** and **Spread out** of **Gaps***

The way that **waves spread out** as they come through a **narrow gap** or go round obstacles is called **diffraction**. **All** waves diffract, but it's not always easy to observe.

Use a **Ripple Tank** To Show Diffraction of **Water Waves**

You can make diffraction patterns in ripple tanks.
The **amount** of diffraction depends on the **wavelength** of the wave compared with the **size of the gap**.

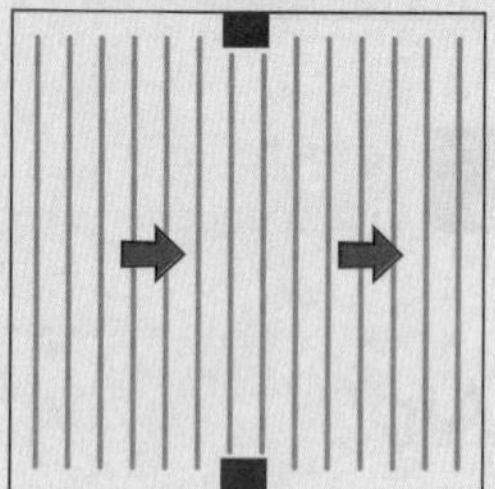

When the gap is **a lot bigger** than the **wavelength**, diffraction is **unnoticeable**.

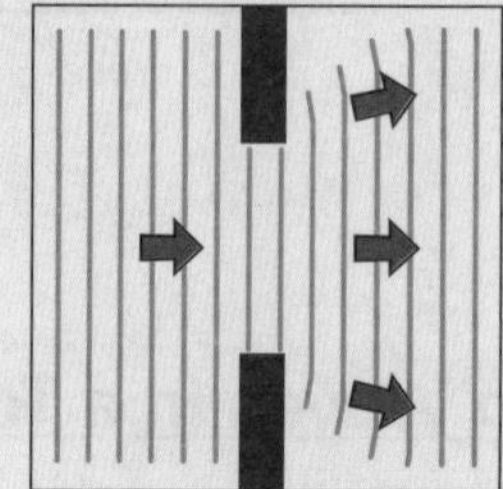

You get **noticeable diffraction** through a gap **several** wavelengths wide.

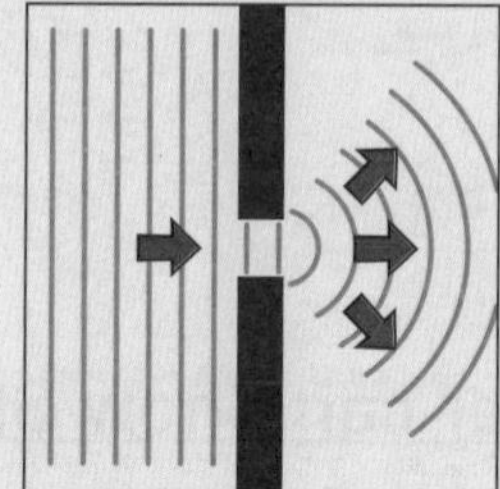

You get the **most** diffraction when the gap is **the same** size as the **wavelength**.

If the gap is **smaller** than the wavelength, the waves are mostly just **reflected back**.

When **sound** passes through a **doorway**, the **size of gap** and the **wavelength** are usually roughly **equal**, so **a lot** of **diffraction** occurs. That's why you have no trouble **hearing** someone through an **open door** to the next room, even if the other person is out of your **line of sight**. The reason that you can't **see** him or her is that when **light** passes through the doorway, it is passing through a **gap** around a **hundred million times bigger** than its wavelength — the amount of diffraction is **tiny**.

Demonstrate **Diffraction** in **Light** Using **Laser Light**

1) Diffraction in **light** can be demonstrated by shining a **laser light** through a very **narrow slit** onto a screen (see page 53). You can alter the amount of diffraction by changing the width of the slit.
2) You can do a similar experiment using a **white light** source instead of the laser (which is monochromatic) and a set of **colour filters**. The size of the slit can be kept constant while the **wavelength** is varied by putting different **colour filters** over the slit.

Warning. Use of coloured filters may result in excessive fun.

*You Get a **Similar** Effect Around an **Obstacle***

When a wave meets an **obstacle**, you get diffraction around the edges.

Behind the obstacle is a '**shadow**', where the wave is blocked. The **wider** the obstacle compared with the wavelength of the wave, the less diffraction you get, and so the **longer** the shadow.

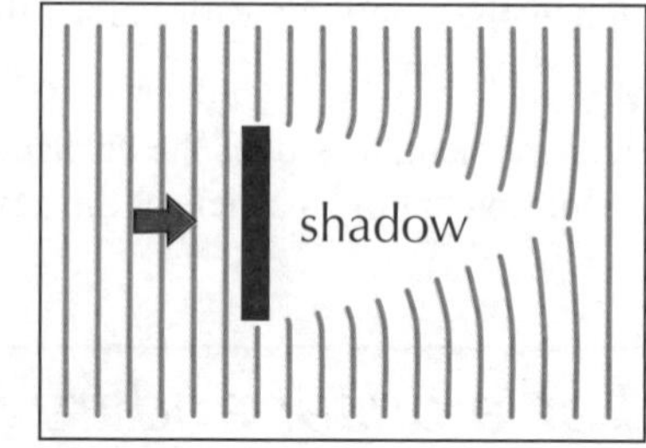

Diffraction

Diffraction is Sometimes **Useful** and Sometimes a Pain...

1) For a **loudspeaker** you want the sound to be heard as widely as possible, so you aim to **maximise** diffraction.
2) With a **microwave oven** you want to **stop** the **microwaves** diffracting out and frying your kidneys **and** you want to **let light through** so you can **see** your food. A **metal mesh** on the **door** has **gaps too small** for microwaves to diffract through, but **light** slips through because of its **tiny wavelength**.

With **Light Waves** you get a **Pattern** of **Light** and **Dark Fringes**

1) If the **wavelength** of a **light wave** is roughly similar to the size of the **aperture**, you get a **diffraction pattern** of light and dark fringes.
2) The pattern has a **bright central fringe** with alternating **dark and bright fringes** on either side of it.

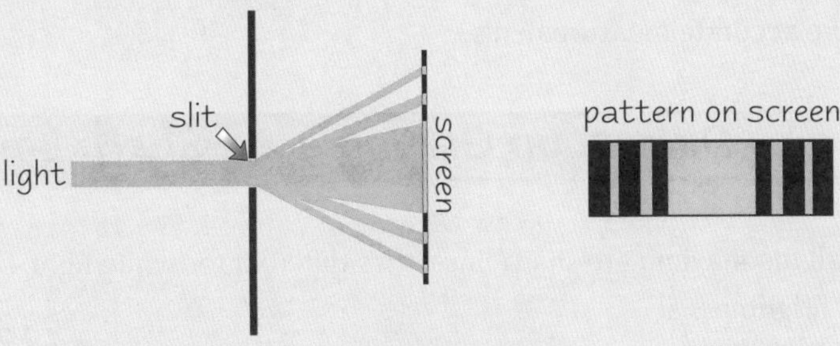

You need to use a coherent light source for this experiment.

3) The **narrower** the slit, the **wider** the diffraction pattern.

You Get a **Similar Pattern** with **Electrons**

1) It's not just with **light** that you get diffraction patterns.
2) In **1927**, two American physicists, **Clinton Davisson** and **Lester Germer**, succeeded in diffracting **electrons**.
3) This was a **huge** discovery. A few years earlier, **Louis de Broglie** had **hypothesised** that electrons would show **wave-like** properties (in the same way that light can show particle-like properties — see page 70), but this was the first **direct evidence** for it.

Electron diffraction patterns look like this

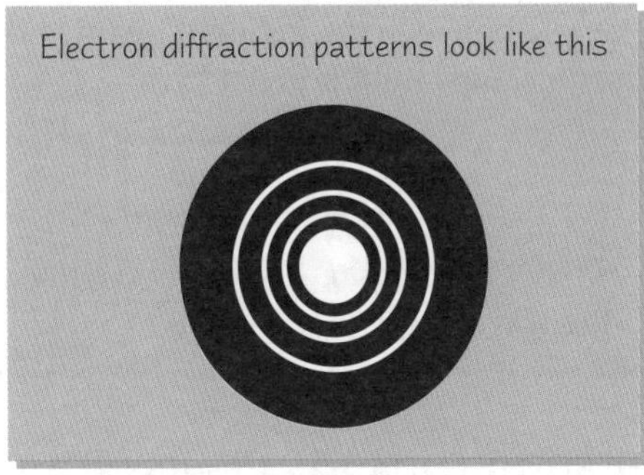

Practice Questions

Q1 What is diffraction?

Q2 Sketch what happens when plane waves meet an obstacle about as wide as one wavelength.

Q3 For a long time some scientists argued that light couldn't be a wave because it did not seem to diffract. Suggest why they might have got this impression.

Q4 Do all waves diffract?

Exam Question

Q1 A mountain lies directly between you and a radio transmitter.

Explain using diagrams why you can pick up long-wave radio broadcasts from the transmitter but not short-wave radio broadcasts. [4 marks]

Even hiding behind a mountain, you can't get away from long-wave radio...

*Diffraction crops up again in particle physics, quantum physics and astronomy, so you **really** need to understand it.*

Diffraction Gratings

Ay... starting to get into some pretty funky stuff now. I like light experiments.

Interference Patterns Get **Sharper** When You Diffract Through **More Slits**

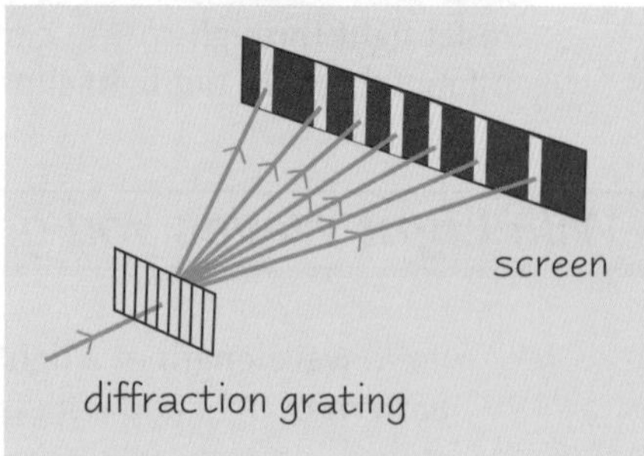

1) You can diffract light through **two or more equally spaced slits** to get an **interference pattern**. The **bright bands** are caused by **constructive interference** of the light waves at that point, and the **dark areas** show where the light waves **destructively interfere**.
2) You get basically the **same shaped** pattern no matter how many slits you use — but the **bright bands** are **brighter** and **narrower** and the **dark areas** between are **darker** as you increase the the number of slits.
3) When **monochromatic light** (one wavelength) is passed through a **grating** with **hundreds** of slits per millimetre, the interference pattern is **really sharp** because there are so **many beams reinforcing** the **pattern**.
4) Sharper fringes make for more **accurate** measurements.

Monochromatic Light on a **Diffraction Grating** gives **Sharp Lines**

1) For **monochromatic** light, all the **maxima** are sharp lines. (It's different for white light — see next page.)
2) There's a line of **maximum brightness** at the centre called the **zero order** line.
3) The lines just **either side** of the central one are called **first order lines**. The **next pair out** are called **second order** lines and so on.
4) For a grating with slits a distance ***d*** apart, the angle between the **incident beam** and **the nth order maximum** is given by:

$$d \sin \theta = n\lambda$$

5) So by observing ***d***, ***θ*** and ***n*** you can **calculate the wavelength** of the light.

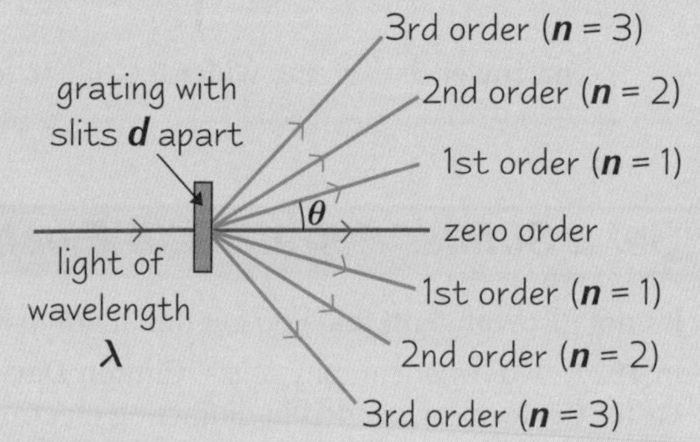

If the grating has N slits per metre, then the slit spacing, d, is just 1/N metres.

WHERE THE EQUATION COMES FROM:

1) At **each slit**, the incoming waves are **diffracted**. These diffracted waves then **interfere** with each other to produce an **interference pattern**.
2) Consider the **first order maximum**. This happens at the **angle** when the waves from one slit line up with waves from the **next slit** that are **exactly one wavelength** behind.

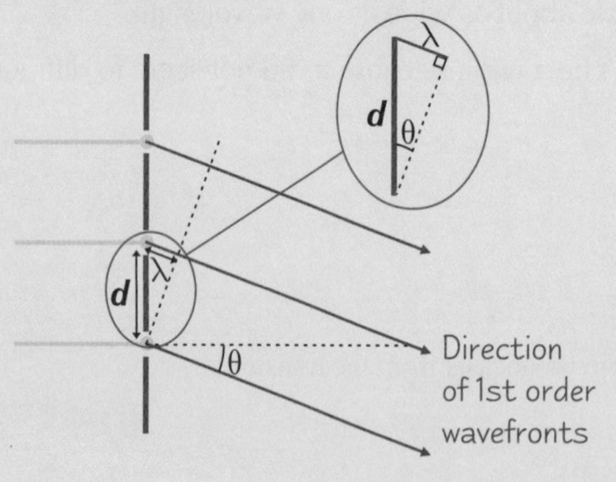

3) Call the **angle** between the **first order maximum** and the **incoming light** θ.
4) Now, look at the **triangle** highlighted in the diagram. The angle is θ (using basic geometry), ***d*** is the slit spacing and the **path difference** is λ.
5) So, for the first maximum, using trig:
$$d \sin \theta = \lambda$$
6) The other maxima occur when the path difference is 2λ, 3λ, 4λ, etc. So to make the equation **general**, just replace λ with *n*λ, where *n* is an integer — the **order** of the maximum.

Diffraction Gratings

You can Draw General Conclusions from d sin θ = nλ

1) If λ is **bigger**, **sin θ** is **bigger**, and so θ is **bigger**. This means that the larger the **wavelength**, the more the pattern will **spread out**.
2) If d is **bigger**, **sin θ** is **smaller**. This means that the **coarser** the **grating**, the **less** the pattern will **spread out**.
3) Values of **sin θ** greater than **1** are **impossible**. So if for a certain n you get a result of **more than 1** for **sin θ** you know that that order **doesn't exist**.

Shining White Light Through a Diffraction Grating Produces Spectra

1) **White light** is really a **mixture** of **colours**. If you **diffract** white light through a **grating** then the patterns due to **different wavelengths** within the white light are **spread out** by **different** amounts.
2) Each **order** in the pattern becomes a **spectrum**, with **red** on the **outside** and **violet** on the **inside**. The **zero order maximum** stays **white** because all the wavelengths just pass straight through.

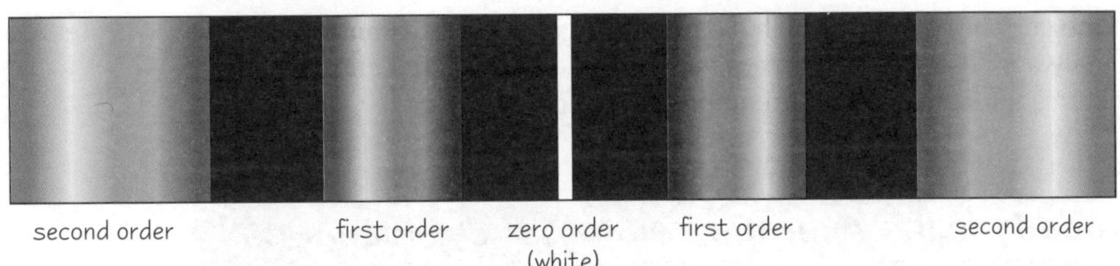

Astronomers and **chemists** often need to study spectra to help identify elements. They use diffraction gratings rather than prisms because they're **more accurate**.

Practice Questions

Q1 How is the diffraction grating pattern for white light different from the pattern for laser light?

Q2 What difference does it make to the pattern if you use a finer grating?

Q3 What equation is used to find the angle between the nth order maximum and the incident beam for a diffraction grating?

Exam Questions

Q1 Yellow laser light of wavelength 600 nm (6×10^{-7} m) is transmitted through a diffraction grating of 4×10^5 lines per metre.

(a) At what angle to the normal are the first and second order bright lines seen? [4 marks]

(b) Is there a fifth order line? [1 mark]

Q2 Visible, monochromatic light is transmitted through a diffraction grating of 3.7×10^5 lines per metre. The first order maximum is at an angle of 14.2° to the incident beam.

The wavelength of the incident light is
A 3.83×10^{-5} m **B** 6.83×10^{-6} m **C** 6.63×10^{-7} m **D** 3.63×10^{-8} m [2 marks]

Ooooooooooooo — pretty patterns...

Yes, it's the end of another beautiful section — woohoo. Three important points for you to take away — 1) the more slits you have, the sharper the image, 2) one lovely equation to learn, and 3) white light makes a pretty spectrum. Make sure you get everything in this section — there's some good stuff coming up in the next one and I wouldn't want you to be distracted.

Charge, Current and Potential Difference

You wouldn't reckon there was that much to know about electricity... just plug something in, and bosh — electricity. Ah well, never mind the age of innocence — here are all the gory details...

Current is the Rate of Flow of Charge

The **current** in a **wire** is like **water** flowing in a **pipe**. The **amount** of water that flows depends on the **flow rate** and the **time**. It's the same with electricity — **current is the rate of flow of charge**.

$$\Delta Q = I\Delta t \quad \text{or} \quad I = \frac{\Delta Q}{\Delta t}$$

Where ΔQ is the charge in coulombs, I is the current and Δt is the time taken.

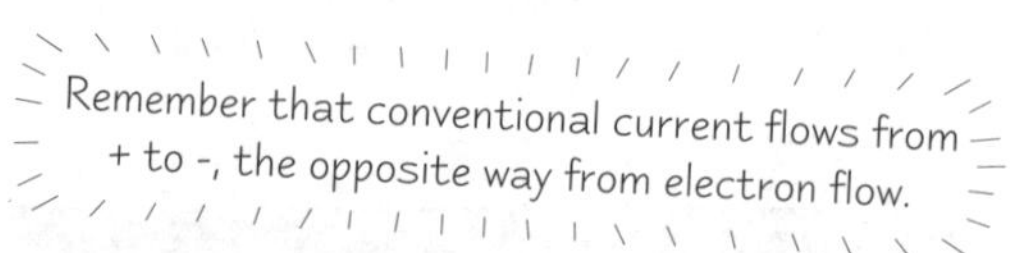

The **Coulomb** is the **Unit** of Charge

One **coulomb** (**C**) is defined as the **amount of charge** that passes in **1 second** when the **current** is **1 ampere**.

You can measure the current flowing through a part of a circuit using an **ammeter**. Remember — you always need to attach an ammeter in **series** (so that the current through the ammeter is the same as the current through the component).

The Drift Velocity is the Average Velocity of the Electrons

When **current** flows through a wire, you might imagine the **electrons** all moving in the **same direction** in an orderly manner. Nope. In fact, they move **randomly** in **all directions**, but tend to **drift** one way. The **drift velocity** is just the **average velocity** and it's **much, much less** than the electrons' **actual speed**. (Their actual speed is about 10^6 ms^{-1}!)

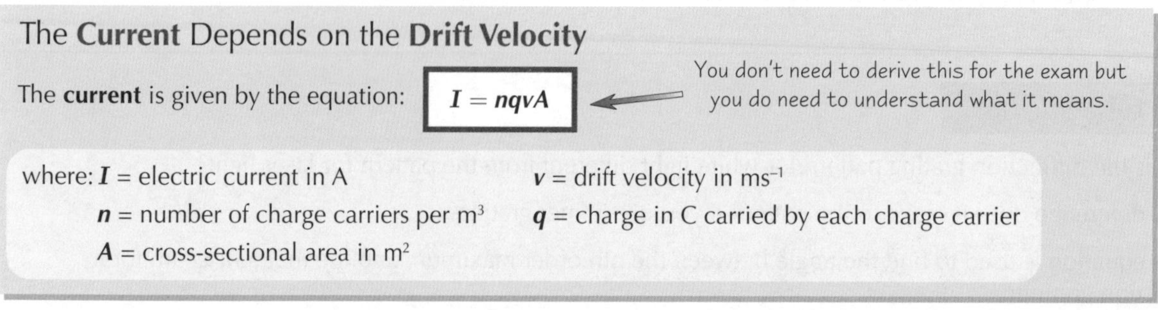

The **Current** Depends on the **Drift Velocity**

The **current** is given by the equation: $I = nqvA$

You don't need to derive this for the exam but you do need to understand what it means.

where: I = electric current in A
n = number of charge carriers per m^3
A = cross-sectional area in m^2
v = drift velocity in ms^{-1}
q = charge in C carried by each charge carrier

See what the **Equation Means** by Changing **One Variable** at a Time

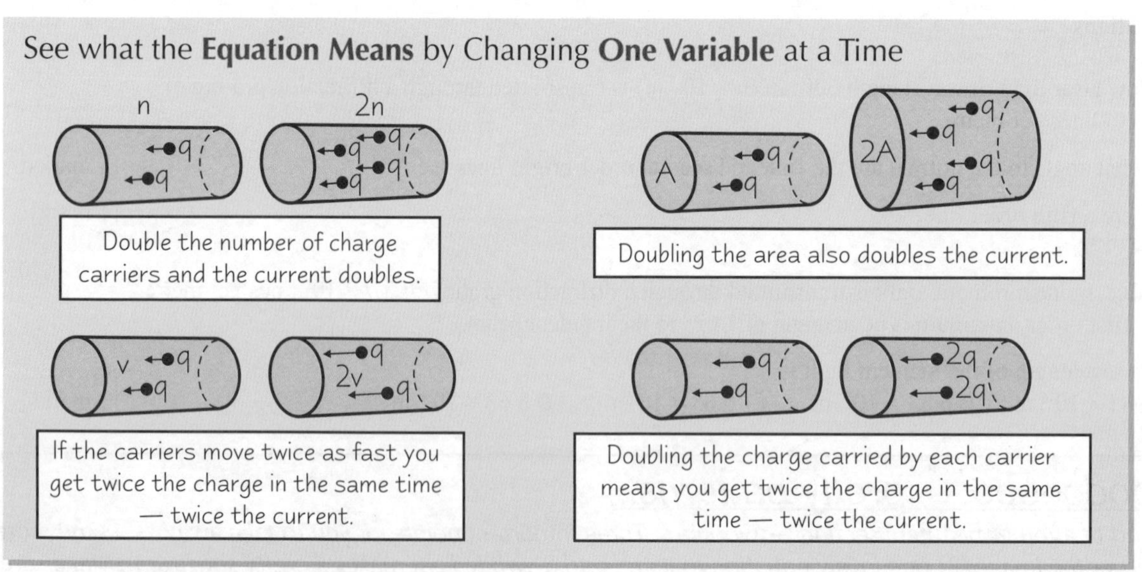

Double the number of charge carriers and the current doubles.

Doubling the area also doubles the current.

If the carriers move twice as fast you get twice the charge in the same time — twice the current.

Doubling the charge carried by each carrier means you get twice the charge in the same time — twice the current.

Charge, Current and Potential Difference

Different Materials *have Different Numbers of* ***Charge Carriers***

1) In a **metal**, the **charge carriers** are **free electrons** — they're the ones from the **outer shell** of each atom. Thinking about the formula $I = nAvq$, there are **loads** of charge carriers, making n **big**. The **drift velocity** only needs to be **small**, even for a **high current**.
2) **Semiconductors** have **fewer charge carriers** than metals, so the **drift velocity** will need to be **higher** if you're going to have the **same current**.
3) A **perfect insulator** wouldn't have **any charge carriers**, so $n = 0$ in the formula and you'd get **no current**. **Real** insulators have a **very small** n.

Charge Carriers *in Liquids and Gases are* ***Ions***

1) **Ionic crystals** like sodium chloride are **insulators**. Once **molten**, though, the liquid **conducts**. Positive and negative **ions** are the **charge carriers**. The **same thing** happens in an **ionic solution** like copper sulphate solution.
2) **Gases** are **insulators**, but if you apply a **high enough voltage** electrons get **ripped out** of **atoms**, giving you **ions** along a path. You get a **spark**.

Potential Difference *is the* ***Energy*** *per* ***Unit Charge***

To make electric charge flow through a conductor, you need to do work on it. **Potential difference** (p.d.), or **voltage**, is defined as the **energy converted per unit charge moved**.

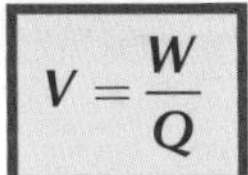

$$V = \frac{W}{Q}$$

W is the energy in joules. It's the work you do moving the charge.

Back to the 'water analogy' again. The p.d. is like the pressure that's forcing water along the pipe.

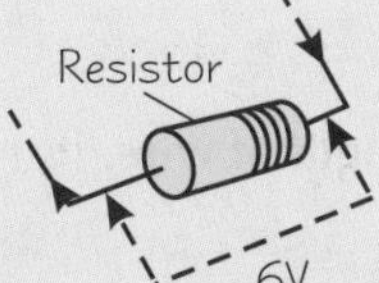

Here you do 6 J of work moving each coulomb of charge through the resistor, so the p.d. across it is 6 V. The energy gets converted to heat.

Definition of the **Volt**

The **potential difference** across a component is **1 volt** when you convert **1 joule** of energy moving **1 coulomb** of charge through the component.

$$1\ \text{V} = 1\ \text{J C}^{-1}$$

Practice Questions

Q1 Describe in words how current and charge are related.

Q2 Define the coulomb.

Q3 Explain what drift velocity is.

Q4 Define potential difference.

Exam Questions

Q1 A battery delivers 4500 C of electric charge to a circuit in 10 minutes. Calculate the average current. [2 marks]

Q2 Copper has 1.0×10^{29} free electrons per m^3. Calculate the drift velocity of the electrons in a copper wire of cross-sectional area $5.0 \times 10^{-6}\ m^2$ when it is carrying a current of 13 A. (electron charge = 1.6×10^{-19} C) [3 marks]

Q3 An electric motor runs off a 12 V d.c. supply and has an overall efficiency of 75%. Calculate how much electric charge will pass through the motor when it does 90 J of work. [3 marks]

I can't even be bothered to make the current joke...

Talking of currant jokes, I saw this bottle of wine the other day called 'raisin d'être' — 'raison d'être' of course meaning 'reason for living', but spelled slightly different to make 'raisin', meaning 'grape'. Ho ho. Chuckled all the way out of Tesco.

Resistance and Resistivity

"You will be assimilated. Resistance is futile."
Sorry, I couldn't resist it (no pun intended), and I couldn't think of anything useful to write anyway. This resistivity stuff gets a bit more interesting when you start thinking about temperature and light dependence, but for now, just learn this.

Everything has Resistance

1) If you put a **potential difference** (p.d.) across an **electrical component**, a **current** will flow.
2) **How much** current you get for a particular **p.d.** depends on the **resistance** of the component.
3) You can think of a component's **resistance** as a **measure** of how **difficult** it is to get a **current** to **flow** through it.

Mathematically, **resistance** is: $R = \frac{V}{I}$

This equation really **defines** what is meant by resistance.

4) **Resistance** is measured in **ohms** (Ω).

A component has a resistance of **1Ω** if a **potential difference** of **1 V** makes a **current** of **1 A** flow through it.

Three Things Determine Resistance

If you think about a nice, **simple electrical component**, like a **length of wire**, its **resistance** depends on:

1) **Length** (l). The **longer** the wire the **more difficult** it is to make a **current flow**.
2) **Area** (A). The **wider** the wire the **easier** it will be for the electrons to pass along it.
3) **Resistivity** (ρ). This **depends** on the **material**. The **structure** of the material of the wire may make it easy or difficult for charge to flow. In general, resistivity depends on **environmental factors** as well, like **temperature** and **light intensity**.

The **resistivity** of a material is defined as the **resistance** of a **1 m length** with a **1 m² cross-sectional area**. It is measured in **ohm metres** (Ωm).

$$\rho = \frac{RA}{l}$$

where A = cross-sectional area in m², l = length in m

You will more **usually** see the equation in the **form**: $R = \rho \frac{l}{A}$

Typical values for the **resistivity** of **conductors** are **really small**.
For example, the resistivity of **copper** (at 25 °C) is just 1.72×10^{-8} Ωm.

If you **calculate** a **resistance** for a **conductor** and end up with something **really small** (e.g. 1×10^{-7} Ω), go back and **check** that you've **converted** your **area** into **m²**.
It's really easy to make mistakes with this equation by leaving the area in **cm²** or **mm²**.

Resistance and Resistivity

For an *Ohmic Conductor*, *R* is a *Constant*

A chap called **Ohm** did most of the early work on resistance. He developed a rule to **predict** how the **current** would **change** as the applied **potential difference increased**, for **certain types** of conductor.

The rule is now called **Ohm's Law** and the conductors that **obey** it (mostly metals) are called **ohmic conductors**.

Provided the **temperature** is **constant**, the **current** through an ohmic conductor is **directly proportional** to the **potential difference** across it.

$$R = \frac{V}{I}$$

1) As you can see from the graph, **doubling** the **p.d. doubles** the **current**.
2) What this means is that the **resistance** is **constant**.
3) Often **external factors**, such as **light level** or **temperature** will have a **significant effect** on resistance, so you need to remember that Ohm's law is **only** true for **ohmic conductors** at **constant temperature**.

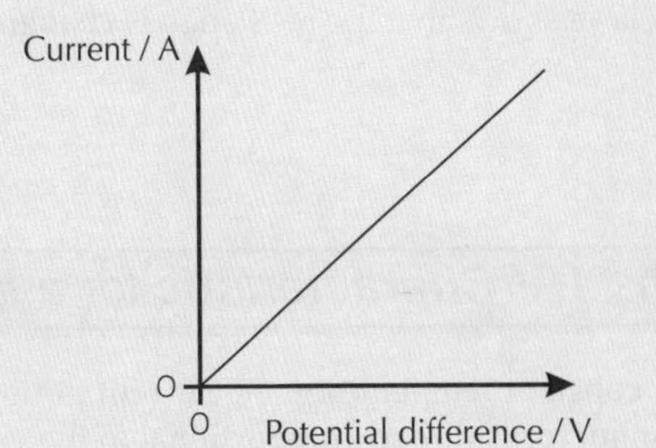

Practice Questions

Q1 Name one environmental factor likely to alter the resistance of a component.

Q2 What is special about an ohmic conductor?

Q3 What three factors does the resistance of a length of wire depend on?

Q4 What are the units for resistivity?

Exam Questions

Q1 Aluminium has a resistivity of $2.8 \times 10^{-8}\ \Omega$m at 20 °C.

Calculate the resistance of a pure aluminium wire of length 4 m and diameter 1 mm, at 20 °C. [3 marks]

Q2 The table below shows some measurements taken by a student during an experiment investigating an unknown electrical component.

Potential Difference (V)	Current (mA)
2.0	2.67
7.0	9.33
11.0	14.67

(a) Use the first row of the table to calculate the resistance of the component when a p.d. of 2 V is applied. [2 marks]

(b) By means of further calculation, or otherwise, decide whether the component is an ohmic conductor. [3 marks]

For ripping results — revise resistance...

One thing that always gets me is the difference between resistivity and resistance — they're easy to mix up. Remember, resistivity is a property of a material — the resistance of a component depends on the resistivity of the material in it.

I/V Characteristics

Woohoo — real physics. This stuff's actually kind of interesting.

I/V Graphs Show how Resistance Varies

The term '***I/V* characteristic**' refers to a **graph** which shows how the **current** (***I***) flowing through a **component changes** as the **potential difference** (***V***) across it is increased.

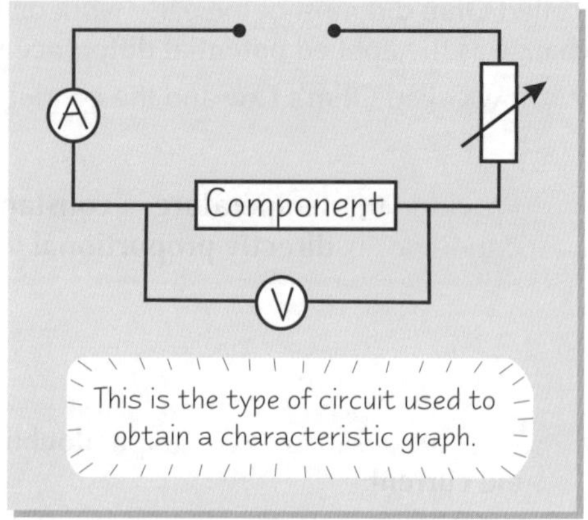

The **shallower** the **gradient** of a characteristic ***I/V*** graph, the **greater** the **resistance** of the component.

A **curve** shows that the resistance is **changing**.

The *I/V* Characteristic for a Metallic Conductor is a Straight Line

At **constant temperature**, the **current** through a **metallic conductor** is **directly proportional** to the **voltage**. The fact that the characteristic graph is a **straight line** tells you that the **resistance doesn't change**. **Metallic conductors** are **ohmic** — they have **constant resistance provided** their temperature doesn't change.

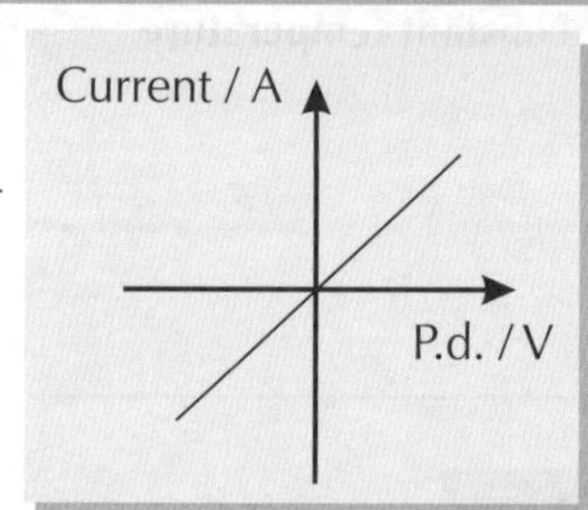

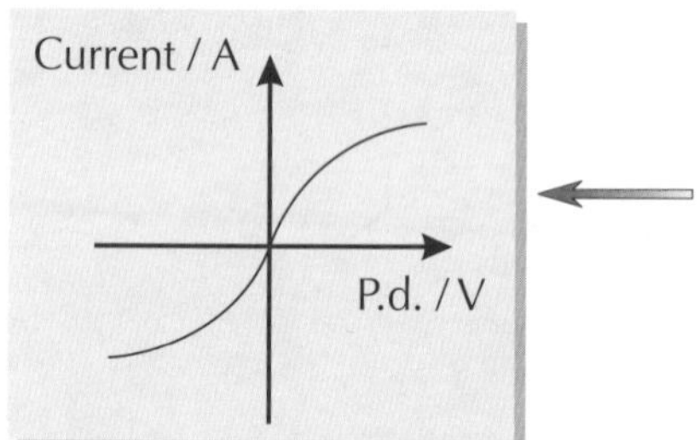

The characteristic graph for a **filament lamp** is a **curve**, which starts **steep** but gets **shallower** as the **voltage rises**. The **filament** in a lamp is just a **coiled up** length of **metal wire**, so you might think it should have the **same characteristic graph** as a **metallic conductor**. It doesn't because it **gets hot**. **Current** flowing through the lamp **increases** its **temperature**.

The **resistance** of a **metal increases** as the **temperature increases**.

The Temperature Affects the Charge Carriers

1) **Charge** is carried through **metals** by **free electrons** in a **lattice** of **positive ions**.
2) Heating up a metal doesn't affect how many electrons there are, but it does make it **harder** for them to **move about**. The **ions vibrate more** when heated, so the electrons **collide** with them more often, **losing energy**.

The **resistance** of most metallic conductors **goes up linearly** with **temperature**.

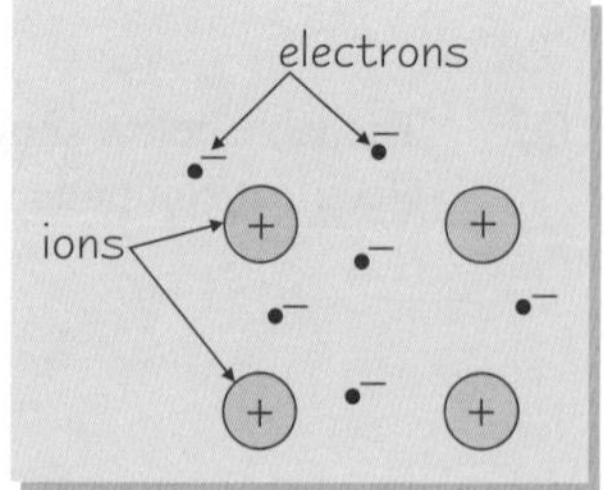

Semiconductors are Used in Sensors

Semiconductors are **nowhere near** as good at **conducting** electricity as **metals**. This is because there are far, far **fewer charge carriers** available. However, if **energy** is supplied to the semiconductor, **more charge carriers** are often **released**. This means that they make **excellent sensors** for detecting **changes** in their **environment**.

You need to know about **three** semiconductor components — **thermistors**, **LDRs** and **diodes**.

I/V Characteristics

The Resistance of a Thermistor Depends on Temperature

Thermistor circuit symbol:

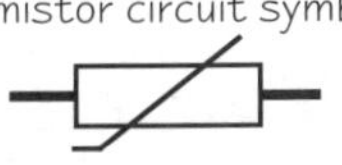

A **thermistor** is a **resistor** with a **resistance** that depends on its **temperature**. You only need to know about **NTC** thermistors — NTC stands for 'Negative Temperature Coefficient'. This means that the **resistance decreases** as the **temperature goes up**. The characteristic graph for an NTC thermistor curves upwards.

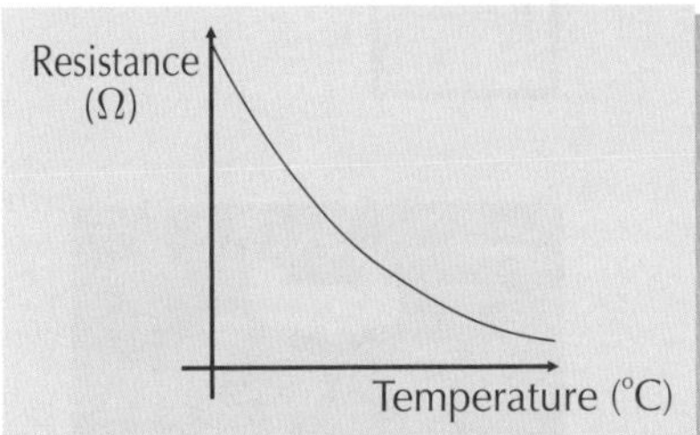

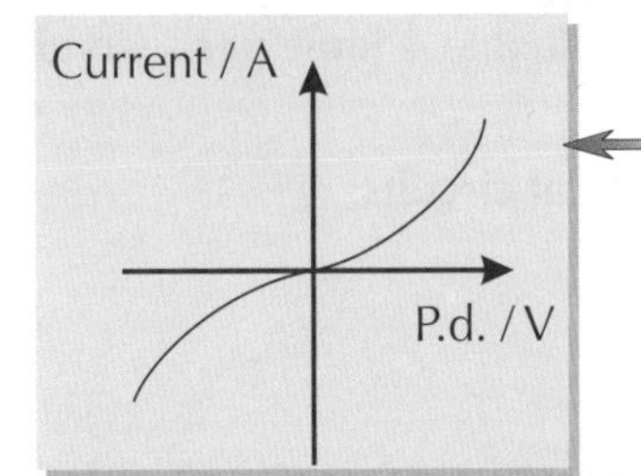

Increasing the current through the thermistor increases its temperature. The increasing gradient of this characteristic graph tells you that the resistance is decreasing.

Warming the thermistor gives more **electrons** enough **energy** to **escape** from their atoms. This means that there are **more charge carriers** available, so the resistance is lower.

The Resistance of an LDR depends on Light Intensity

LDR circuit symbol:

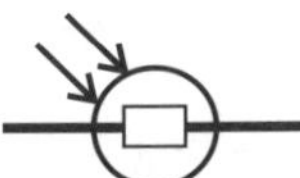

LDR stands for **Light-Dependent Resistor**. The **greater** the intensity of **light** shining on an LDR, the **lower** its **resistance**.

The explanation for this is similar to that for the thermistor. In this case, **light** provides the **energy** that releases more electrons. More charge carriers means a lower resistance.

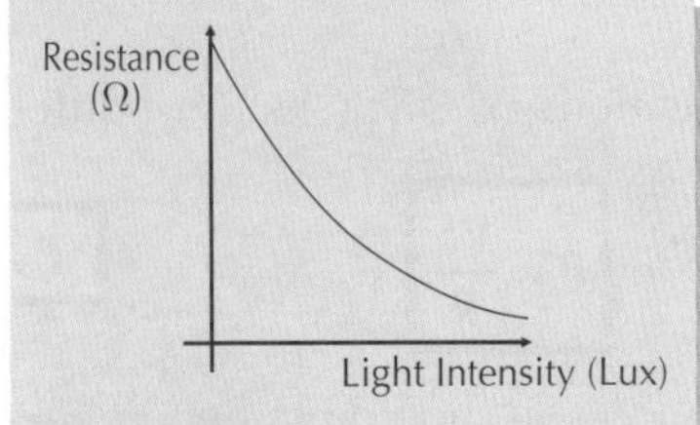

Large Dayglow Rabbit

Diodes Only Let Current Flow in One Direction

Diode and LED circuit symbols:

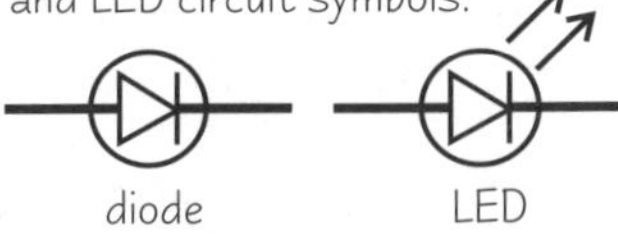

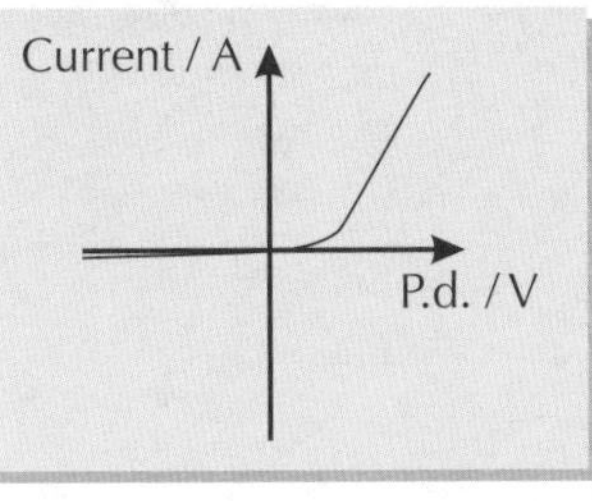

Diodes (including light emitting diodes (LEDs)) are designed to let **current flow** in **one direction** only. You don't need to be able to explain how they work, just what they do.

1) **Forward bias** is the **direction** in which the **current** is **allowed to flow**.
2) **Most** diodes require a **threshold voltage** of about **0.6 V** in the **forward direction** before they will conduct.
3) In **reverse bias**, the **resistance** of the diode is **very high** and the current that flows is **very tiny**.

Practice Questions

Q1 Sketch the circuit used to determine the ***I/V*** characteristics of a component.

Q2 Draw an ***I/V*** characteristic graph for a diode.

Q3 What is an LDR?

Q4 If an ***I/V*** graph is curved, what does this tell you about the resistance?

Exam Question

Q1 (a) Sketch a characteristic ***I/V*** graph for a filament lamp. [1 mark]

(b) State how the resistance changes as the temperature increases. [1 mark]

(c) Explain why this happens. [2 marks]

Thermistor man — temperature-dependent Mr Man...

Learn the graphs on these pages, and make sure you can explain them. Whether it's a light-dependent resistor or a thermistor, the same principle applies. More energy releases more charge carriers, and more charge carriers means a lower resistance.

Electrical Energy and Power

Power and energy are pretty familiar concepts — and here they are again. Same principles, just different equations.

Power is the Rate of Transfer of Energy

Power (*P*) is **defined** as the **rate** of **transfer** of **energy**.
It's measured in **watts** (*W*), where **1 watt** is equivalent to **1 joule per second**.

or $P = \frac{W}{t}$

There's a really simple formula for **power** in **electrical circuits**:

$$P = VI$$

This makes sense, since:

1) **Potential difference** (*V*) is defined as the **energy transferred** per **coulomb**.
2) **Current** (*I*) is defined as the **number** of **coulombs** transferred per **second**.
3) So **p.d.** × **current** is **energy transferred per second**, i.e. **power**.

He didn't know when, he didn't know where... but one day this PEt would get his revenge.

You know from the definition of **resistance** that: $V = IR$

Combining the **two equations** gives you loads of **different ways** to **calculate power**.

$$P = VI \qquad P = \frac{V^2}{R} \qquad P = I^2R$$

Obviously, which equation you should use depends on what **quantities** you're given in the **question**.

Phew... that's quite a few equations to learn and love. And as if they're not exciting enough, here are some examples to get your teeth into...

Example 1

A 24 W car headlamp is connected to a 12 V car battery.
(a) How much energy will the lamp convert into light and heat energy in 2 hours?
(b) Find the total resistance of the lamp.

(a) Number of seconds in 2 hours = 120 × 60 = 7200 s
$E = P \times t = 24 \times 7200 = 172\ 800$ J = **172.8 kJ**

(b) Rearrange the equation $P = \frac{V^2}{R}$, $R = \frac{V^2}{P} = \frac{12^2}{24} = \frac{144}{24} = \underline{6\ \Omega}$

Example 2

A robotic mutant Santa from the future converts 750 J of electrical energy into heat every second.
(a) What is the power rating of the robotic mutant Santa?
(b) All of the robotic mutant Santa's components are connected in series, with a total resistance of 30 Ω. What current flows through his wire veins?

(a) Power (W) = $E \div t = 750 \div 1 =$ **750 W**

(b) Rearrange the equation $P = I^2R$, $I = \sqrt{\frac{P}{R}} = \sqrt{\frac{750}{30}} = \sqrt{25} = \underline{5\text{ A}}$

Electrical Energy and Power

Energy is Easy to **Calculate** if you Know the **Power**

Sometimes it's the **total energy** transferred that you're interested in. In this case you simply need to **multiply** the **power** by the **time**. So:

$W = VIt$ (or $W = \frac{V^2}{R}t$ or $W = I^2Rt$)

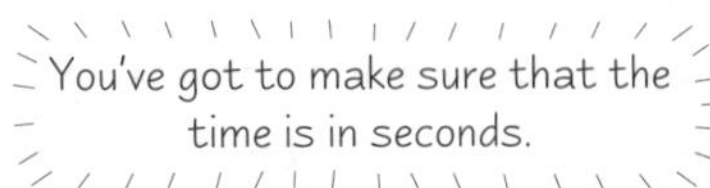

Example

Betty pops the kettle on to make a brew.
It takes 4.5 minutes for the kettle to boil the water inside it.
A current of 4 A flows through the kettle's heating element once it is connected to the mains (230 V).

(a) What is the power rating of the kettle?

(b) How much energy does the kettle's heating element transfer to the water in the time it takes to boil?

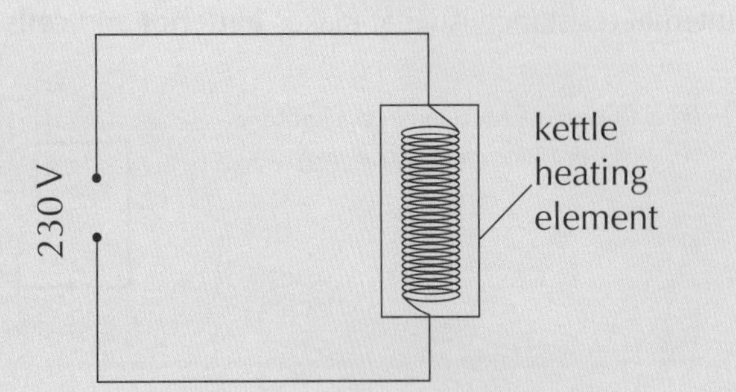

(a) Use $P = V \times I = 230 \times 4 =$ **920 W**

(b) Time the kettle takes to boil in seconds = 4.5 × 60 = 270 seconds.
Use the equation $W = Pt = VIt = 230 \times 4 \times 270 = 248\ 400$ J = **248.4 kJ**

Practice Questions

Q1 Write down the equation linking power, current and resistance.

Q2 What equation links power, voltage and resistance?

Q3 Power is measured in watts. What is 1 watt equivalent to?

Exam Questions

Q1 This question concerns a mains powered hairdryer, the circuit diagram for which is given below.

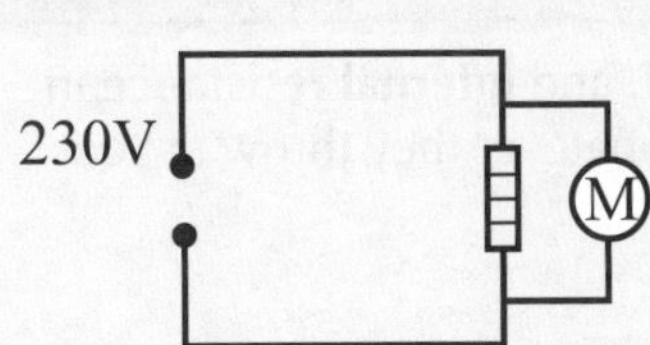

(a) The heater has a power of 920 W in normal operation. Calculate the current in the heater. [2 marks]

(b) The motor has a resistance of 190 Ω. What current will flow in the motor when the hairdryer is used? [2 marks]

(c) Show that the total power of the hairdryer in normal operation is just under 1.2 kW. [2 marks]

Q2 A 12 V car battery supplies a current of 48 A for 2 seconds to the car's starter motor.
The total resistance of the connecting wires is 0.01 Ω.

(a) The energy transferred from the battery is: **A** 1250 J **B** 1.2 kJ **C** 1512 J **D** 1152 J [1 mark]

(b) The energy wasted as heat in the wires is: **A** 64 J **B** 46 J **C** 56 J **D** 38 J [1 mark]

Ultimate cosmic powers...

Whenever you get equations in this book, you know you're gonna have to learn them. Fact of life. I used to find it helped to stick big lists of equations all over my walls in the run-up to the exams. But as that's possibly the least cool wallpaper imaginable, I don't advise inviting your friends round till after the exams...

E.m.f. and Internal Resistance

There's resistance everywhere — inside batteries, in all the wires and in the components themselves. No one's for giving current an easy ride.

From now on, I'm assuming that the resistance of the wires in the circuit is zero. In practice, they do have a small resistance.

Batteries have **Resistance**

Resistance comes from **electrons colliding** with **atoms** and **losing energy**.

In a **battery**, **chemical energy** is used to make **electrons move**. As they move, they collide with atoms inside the battery — so batteries **must** have resistance. This is called **internal resistance**.

Internal resistance is what makes **batteries** and **cells warm up** when they're used.

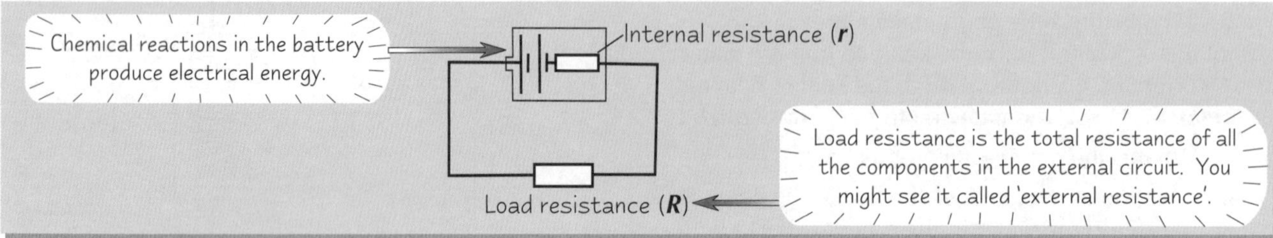

1) The amount of **electrical energy** the battery produces for each **coulomb** of charge is called its **electromotive force** or **e.m.f.** (ε). Be careful — e.m.f. **isn't** actually a force. It's measured in **volts**.
2) The **potential difference** across the **load resistance** (***R***) is the **energy transferred** when **one coulomb** of charge flows through the **load resistance**. This potential difference is called the **terminal p.d.** (***V***).
3) If there was **no internal resistance**, the **terminal p.d**. would be the **same** as the **e.m.f.** However, in **real** power supplies, there's **always some energy lost** overcoming the internal resistance.
4) The **energy wasted per coulomb** overcoming the internal resistance is called the **lost volts** (***v***).

Conservation of energy tells us:

energy per coulomb supplied by the source = **energy per coulomb used in load resistance** + **energy per coulomb wasted in internal resistance**

There are Loads of **Calculations** with **E.m.f.** and **Internal Resistance**

Examiners can ask you to do **calculations** with **e.m.f.** and **internal resistance** in loads of **different** ways. You've got to be ready for whatever they throw at you.

$$\varepsilon = V + v \qquad \varepsilon = I(R + r)$$
$$V = \varepsilon - v \qquad V = \varepsilon - Ir$$

These are all basically the **same equation**, just written differently. If you're given enough information you can calculate the e.m.f. (ε), terminal p.d. (***V***), lost volts (***v***), current (***I***), load resistance (***R***) or internal resistance (***r***). Which equation you should use depends on what information you've got, and what you need to calculate.

Most Power Supplies Need **Low Internal Resistance**

A **car battery** has to deliver a **really high current** — so it needs to have a **low internal resistance**. The cells used to power a **torch** or a **personal stereo** are the **same**. **Generally**, **batteries** have an **internal resistance** of **less than 1 Ω**.

Since **internal resistance** causes **energy loss**, you'd think **all** power supplies should have a **low internal resistance**.

High voltage power supplies are the **exception**. **HT** (high tension) and **EHT** (extremely high tension) **supplies** are designed with **very high** internal resistances. This means that if they're **accidentally short-circuited** only a **very small current** can flow. Much **safer**.

E.m.f. and Internal Resistance

Use this Circuit to Measure Internal Resistance and E.m.f.

By **changing** the value of ***R*** (**load resistance**) in this circuit and **measuring** the **current** (***I***) and **p.d.** (***V***), you can work out the **internal resistance** of the source.

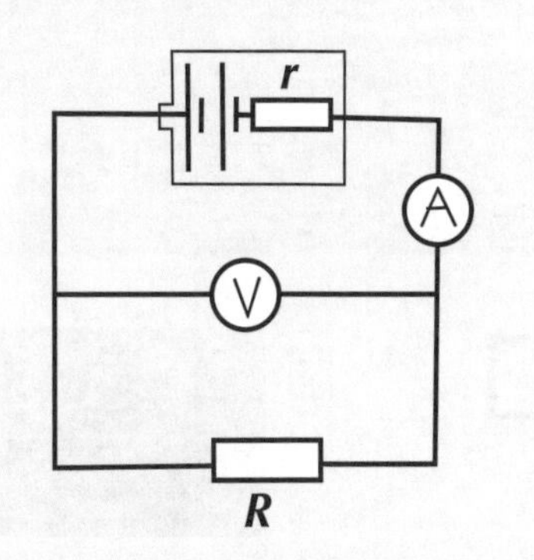

Start with the equation:

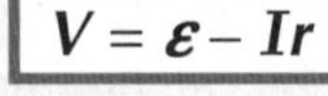

Plot a graph of ***V*** against ***I***.

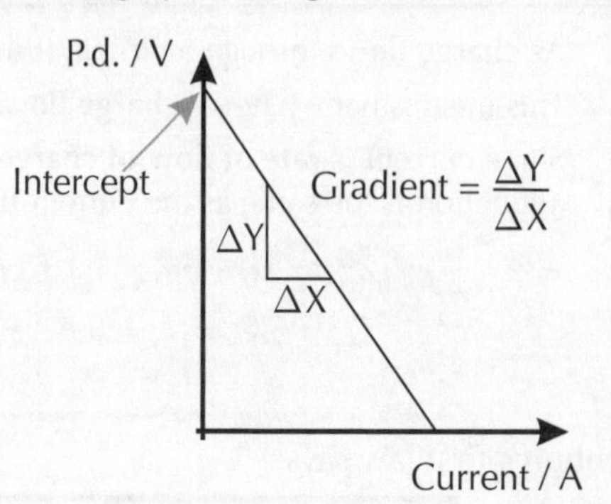

1) Rearrange the equation: $V = -rI + \varepsilon$
2) Since ε and r are constants, that's just the equation of a **straight line** (in the form: $y = mx + c$).
3) So the intercept on the vertical axis is ε.
4) And the gradient is $-r$.

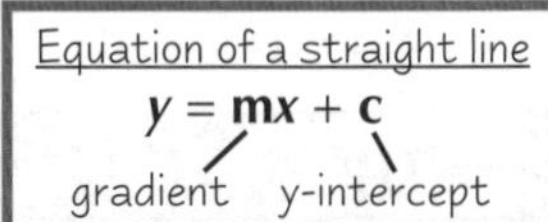

An **easier** way to **measure** the **e.m.f.** of a **power source** is by connecting a high-resistance **voltmeter** across its **terminals**. A **small current flows** through the **voltmeter**, so there must be some **lost volts** — this means you measure a value **very slightly less** than the **e.m.f.** In **practice** the difference **isn't** usually **significant**.

Practice Questions

Q1 What causes internal resistance?

Q2 What is meant by 'lost volts'?

Q3 What is the difference between e.m.f. and terminal p.d.?

Q4 Write the equation used to calculate the terminal p.d. of a power supply.

Exam Questions

Q1 A large battery with an internal resistance of 0.8 Ω and e.m.f. 24 V is used to power a dentist's drill with resistance 4 Ω.

(a) Calculate the current in the circuit when the drill is connected to the power supply. [2 marks]

(b) Calculate the voltage across the drill while it is being used. [1 mark]

Q2 A student mistakenly connects a 10 Ω ray box to an HT power supply of 500 V. The ray box does not light, and the student measures the current flowing to be only 50 mA.

(a) Calculate the internal resistance of the HT power supply. [2 marks]

(b) Explain why this is a sensible internal resistance for an HT power supply. [2 marks]

You're UNBELIEVABLE... [Frantic air guitar]... Ueuuurrrrghhh... Yeah...

Wanting power supplies to have a low internal resistance makes sense — you wouldn't want your MP3 player battery melting if you listened to music for more than half an hour. Make sure you know your e.m.f. equations — they'e an exam fave. A good way to get them learnt is to keep trying to get from one equation to another... dull, but it can help.

Conservation of Energy & Charge in Circuits

There are some things in Physics that are so fundamental that you just have to accept them. Like the fact that there's loads of Maths in it. And that energy is conserved. And that Physicists get more homework than everyone else.

Charge Doesn't 'Leak Away' Anywhere — it's Conserved

1) As **charge flows** through a circuit, it **doesn't** get **used up** or **lost**.
2) This means that whatever **charge flows into** a junction will **flow out** again.
3) Since **current** is **rate of flow of charge**, it follows that whatever **current flows into** a junction is the same as the current **flowing out** of it.

e.g. CHARGE FLOWING IN 1 SECOND

$Q_1 = 6\text{ C} \Rightarrow I_1 = 6\text{ A}$ → $Q_2 = 2\text{ C} \Rightarrow I_2 = 2\text{ A}$ and $Q_3 = 4\text{ C} \Rightarrow I_3 = 4\text{ A}$

$$I_1 = I_2 + I_3$$

Kirchhoff's first law says:

> The total **current entering a junction** = the total **current leaving it.**

Energy conservation is vital.

Energy is Conserved too

1) **Energy is conserved**. You already know that. In **electrical circuits**, **energy** is **transferred round** the circuit. Energy **transferred to** a charge is **e.m.f.**, and energy **transferred from** a charge is **potential difference**.
2) In a **closed loop**, these two quantities must be **equal** if energy is conserved (which it is).

Kirchhoff's second law says:

> The **total e.m.f.** around a **series circuit** = the **sum** of the **p.d.s** across each component.

(or $\varepsilon = \Sigma IR$ in symbols)

Exam Questions get you to Apply Kirchhoff's Laws to Combinations of Resistors

A **typical exam question** will give you a **circuit** with bits of information missing, leaving you to fill in the gaps. Not the most fun... but on the plus side you get to ignore any internal resistance stuff (unless the question tells you otherwise)... hurrah. You need to remember the **following rules**:

SERIES Circuits

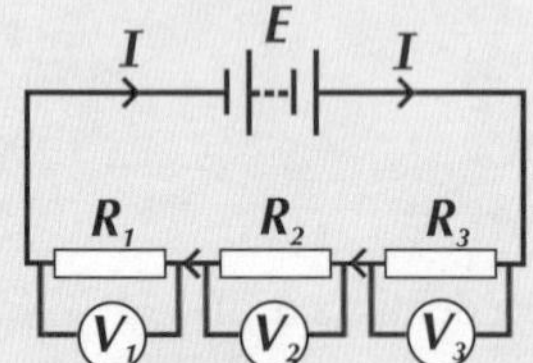

1) **same current** at **all points** of the circuit (since there are no junctions)
2) **e.m.f. split** between **components** (by Kirchhoff's 2nd law), so: $E = V_1 + V_2 + V_3$
3) $V = IR$, so if I is constant: $IR_{total} = IR_1 + IR_2 + IR_3$
4) cancelling the Is gives:

$$R_{total} = R_1 + R_2 + R_3$$

PARALLEL Circuits

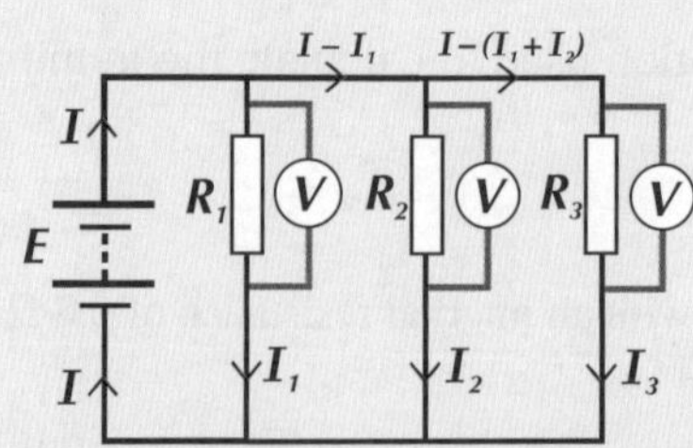

1) **current** is **split** at each **junction**, so: $I = I_1 + I_2 + I_3$
2) **same p.d.** across **all components** (three separate loops — within each loop the e.m.f. equals sum of individual p.d.s)
3) so, $V/R_{total} = V/R_1 + V/R_2 + V/R_3$
4) cancelling the Vs gives:

$$1/R_{total} = 1/R_1 + 1/R_2 + 1/R_3$$

...and there's an example on the next page to make sure you know what to do with all that...

Conservation of Energy & Charge in Circuits

Worked Exam Question

A battery of e.m.f. 16 V and negligible internal resistance is connected in a circuit as shown:

a) Show that the group of resistors between X and Y could be replaced by a single resistor of resistance 15 Ω.

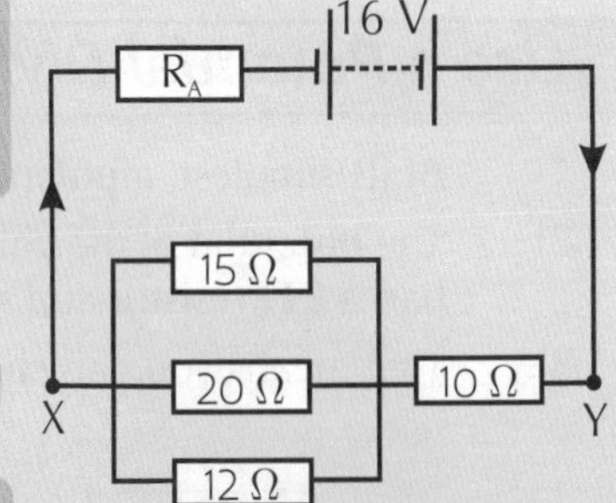

You can find the **combined resistance** of the 15 Ω, 20 Ω and 12 Ω resistors using:

$1/\boldsymbol{R} = 1/\boldsymbol{R_1} + 1/\boldsymbol{R_2} + 1/\boldsymbol{R_3} = 1/15 + 1/20 + 1/12 = 1/5 \quad \Rightarrow \boldsymbol{R} = 5\ \Omega$

So **overall resistance** between **X** and **Y** can be found by $\boldsymbol{R} = \boldsymbol{R_1} + \boldsymbol{R_2} = 5 + 10 = \mathbf{15\ \Omega}$

b) If $R_A = 20\ \Omega$:
(i) calculate the potential difference across R_A,

Careful — there are a few steps here. You need the p.d. across R_A, but you don't know the current through it. So start there: **total resistance in circuit** = 20 + 15 = 35 Ω, **so** current through R_A can be found using $I = V_{total}/R_{total}$:

$I = 16/35$ A

then you can use $V = IR_A$ to find the p.d. across R_A: $V = 16/35 \times 20 = \mathbf{9.1\ V}$

(ii) calculate the current in the 15 Ω resistor.

You know the **current flowing** into the group of three resistors and out of it, but not through the individual branches. But you know that their **combined resistance** is **5** Ω (from part a) so you can work out the p.d. across the group:

$V = IR = 16/35 \times 5 = 16/7$ V

The p.d. across the **whole group** is the same as the p.d. across each **individual resistor**, so you can use this to find the current through the 15 Ω resistor:

$I = V/R = (16/7)/15 = \mathbf{0.15\ A}$

Practice Questions

Q1 State Kirchhoff's laws.

Q2 Find the current through and potential difference across each of two 5 Ω resistors when they are placed in a circuit containing a 5 V battery, and are wired: a) in series, b) in parallel.

Exam Question

Q1 For the circuit on the right:

(a) Calculate the total effective resistance of the three resistors in this combination. [2 marks]

(b) Calculate the main current, I_3. [2 marks]

(c) Calculate the potential difference across the 4 Ω resistor. [1 mark]

(d) Calculate the potential difference across the parallel pair of resistors. [1 mark]

(e) Using your answer from 1 (d), calculate the currents I_1 and I_2. [2 marks]

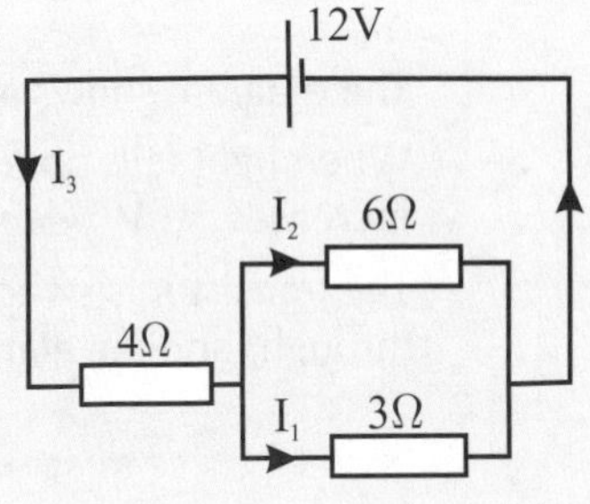

This is a very purple page — needs a bit of yellow I think...

V = IR is the formula you'll use most often in these questions. Make sure you know whether you're using it on the overall circuit, or just one specific component. It's amazingly easy to get muddled up — you've been warned.

The Potential Divider

I remember the days when potential dividers were pretty much the hardest thing they could throw at you. Then along came AS Physics. Hey ho.

Anyway, in context this doesn't seem too hard now, so get stuck in.

Use a **Potential Divider** to get a **Fraction** of a **Source Voltage**

1) At its simplest, a **potential divider** is a circuit with a **voltage source** and a couple of **resistors** in series.
2) The **potential** of the voltage source (e.g. a power supply) is **divided** in the **ratio** of the **resistances**. So, if you had a **2 Ω** resistor and a **3 Ω** resistor, you'd get **2/5** of the p.d. across the **2 Ω** resistor and **3/5** across the **3 Ω**.
3) That means you can **choose** the **resistances** to get the **voltage** you **want** across one of them.

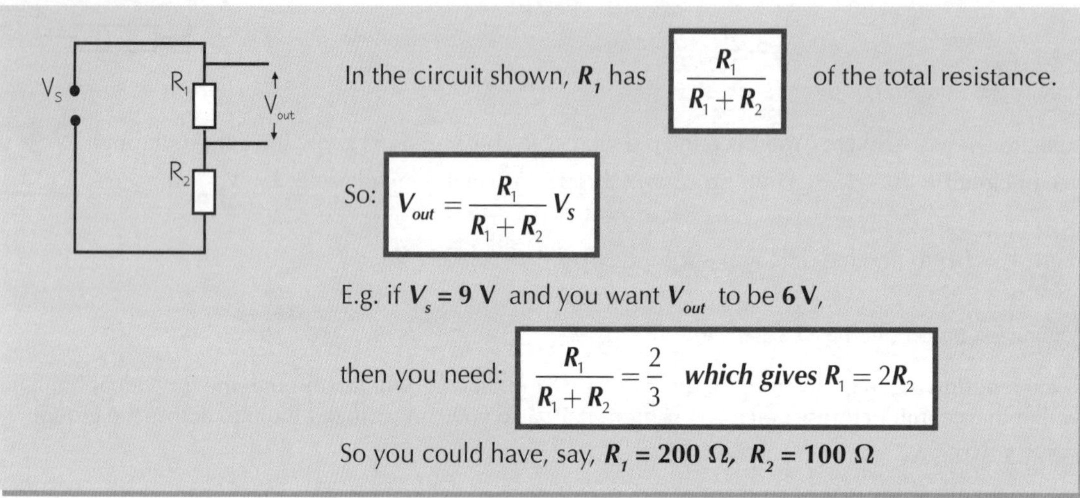

In the circuit shown, R_1 has $\frac{R_1}{R_1 + R_2}$ of the total resistance.

So: $V_{out} = \frac{R_1}{R_1 + R_2} V_S$

E.g. if V_s = **9 V** and you want V_{out} to be **6 V**,

then you need: $\frac{R_1}{R_1 + R_2} = \frac{2}{3}$ *which gives* $R_1 = 2R_2$

So you could have, say, R_1 = **200 Ω**, R_2 = **100 Ω**

4) This circuit is mainly used for **calibrating voltmeters**, which have a **very high resistance**.
5) If you put something with a **relatively low resistance** across R_1 though, you start to run into **problems**. You've **effectively** got **two resistors** in **parallel**, which will **always** have a **total** resistance **less** than R_1. That means that V_{out} will be **less** than you've calculated, and will depend on what's connected across R_1. Hrrumph.

Add an **LDR** or **Thermistor** for a **Light** or **Temperature Switch**

1) A **light-dependent resistor** (LDR) has a very **high resistance** in the **dark**, but a **lower resistance** in the **light**.
2) An **NTC thermistor** has a **high resistance** at **low temperatures**, but a much **lower resistance** at **high temperatures** (it varies in the opposite way to a normal resistor, only much more so).
3) Either of these can be used as one of the **resistors** in a **potential divider**, giving an **output voltage** that **varies** with the **light level** or **temperature**.
4) Add a **transistor** and you've got yourself a **switch**, e.g. to turn on a light or a heating system.

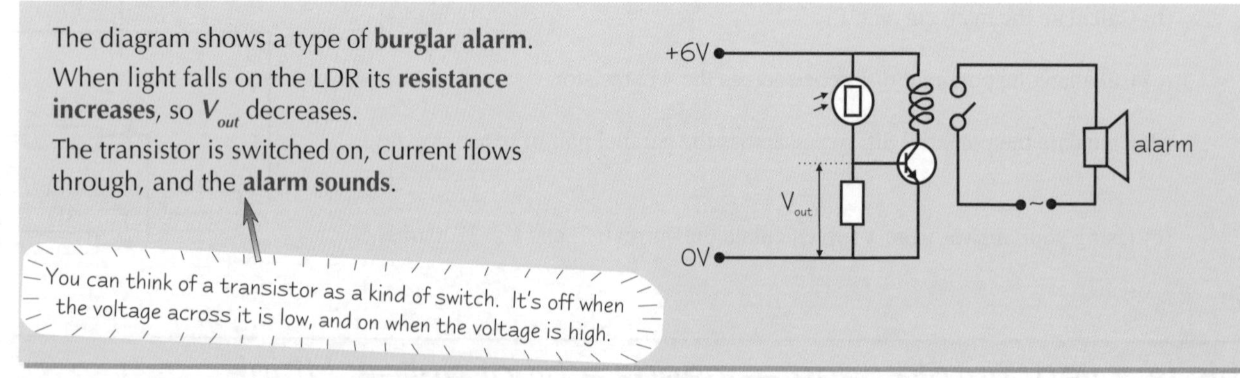

The diagram shows a type of **burglar alarm**. When light falls on the LDR its **resistance increases**, so V_{out} decreases. The transistor is switched on, current flows through, and the **alarm sounds**.

You can think of a transistor as a kind of switch. It's off when the voltage across it is low, and on when the voltage is high.

The Potential Divider

*A **Potentiometer** uses a **Variable Resistor** to give a **Variable Voltage***

1) A **potentiometer** has a variable resistor replacing R_1 and R_2 of the potential divider, but it uses the **same idea** (it's even sometimes **called** a potential divider just to confuse things).
2) You move a **slider** or turn a knob to **adjust** the **relative sizes** of R_1 and R_2. That way you can vary V_{out} from **0 V** up to the source voltage.
3) This is dead handy when you want to be able to **change** a **voltage continuously**, like in the **volume control** of a stereo.

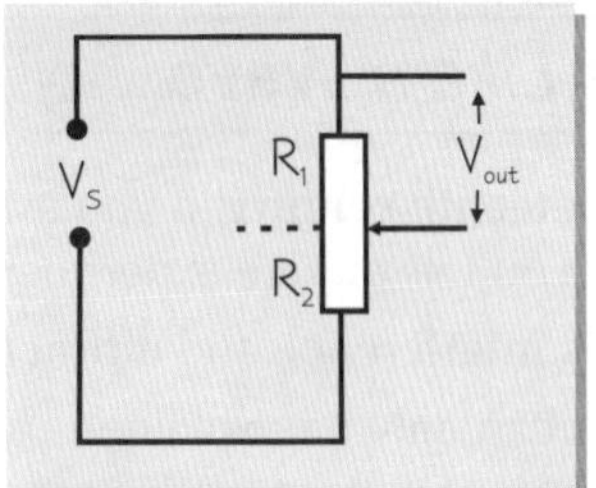

Here, V_S is replaced by the input signal (e.g. from a CD player) and V_{out} is the output to the amplifier and loudspeaker.

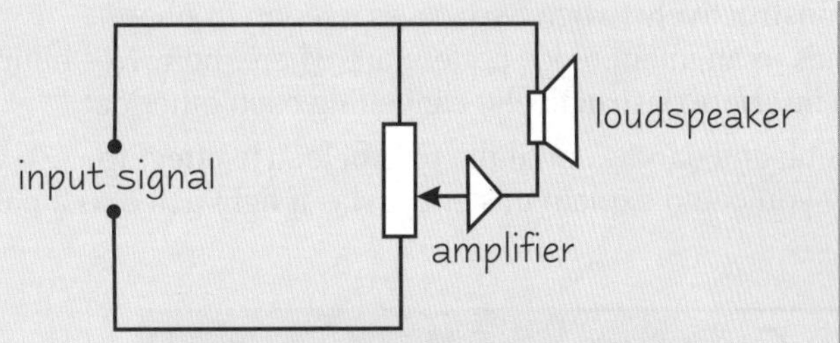

Practice Questions

Q1 Look at the burglar alarm circuit on page 68. How could you change the circuit so that the alarm sounds when the light level decreases?

Q2 The LDR in the burglar alarm circuit has a resistance of 300 Ω when light and 900 Ω when dark. The fixed resistor has a value of 100 Ω. Show that V_{out} (light) = 1.5 V and V_{out} (dark) = 0.6 V.

Exam Questions

Q1 In the circuit on the right, all the resistors have the same value. Calculate the p.d. between:

(i) A and B. [1 mark]

(ii) A and C. [1 mark]

(iii) B and C. [1 mark]

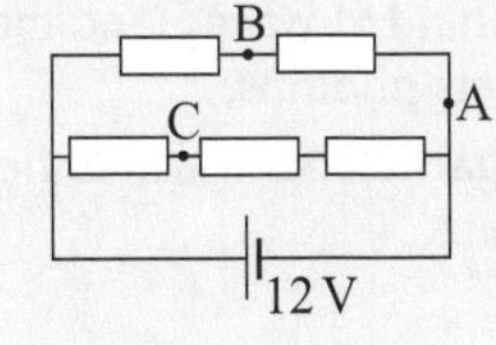

Q2 Look at the circuit on the right.

(a) Calculate the p.d. between A and B as shown by a high resistance voltmeter placed between the two points. [1 mark]

(b) A 40 Ω resistor is now placed between points A and B. Calculate the p.d. across AB and the current flowing through the 40 Ω resistor. [4 marks]

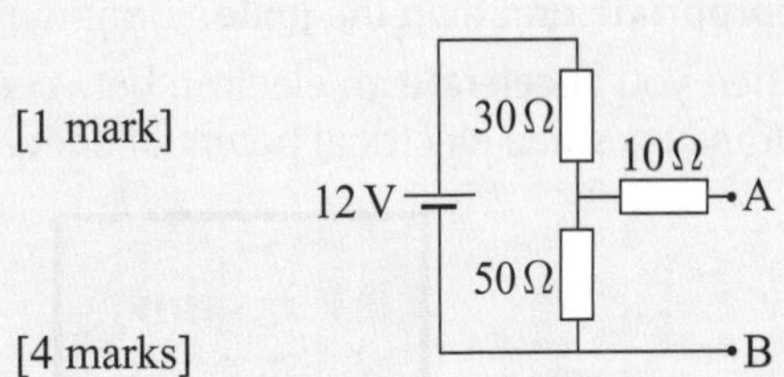

OI... YOU... [bang bang bang]... turn that potentiometer down...

You'll probably have to use a potentiometer in every experiment you do with electricity from now on in, so you'd better get used to them. I can't stand the things myself, but then lab and me don't mix — far too technical.

Light — Wave or Photon

You probably already thought light was a bit weird — but oh no... being a wave that travels at the fastest speed possible isn't enough for light — it has to go one step further and act like a particle too...

Light Behaves Like a **Wave**... or a **Stream of Particles**

1) In the **late nineteenth century**, if you asked what light was, scientists would happily show you lots of nice experiments showing how light must be a **wave**.
2) Light produces **interference** and **diffraction** patterns — **alternating bands** of **dark** and **light**.
3) These patterns can **only** be explained using **waves**.
   Take an interference pattern made by two sources both emitting only one wavelength of light.
   The **bright bands** of the interference pattern are caused by the waves from each source **interfering constructively** (when two waves overlap in phase).
   The **dark bands** in an interference pattern are where the waves hitting that part of the screen are out of phase and **interfere destructively**, cancelling each other out.
4) That was all fine and dandy... until the **photoelectric effect** (p. 72), which mucked up everything.
   The only way you could explain this effect was if light acted as a **particle** — called a **photon**.

A **Photon** is a **Quantum** of **EM Radiation**

1) When Max Planck was investigating **black body radiation** (don't worry — you don't need to know about that just yet), he suggested that **EM waves** can **only** be **released** in **discrete packets**, called **quanta**. A single packet of **EM radiation** is called a **quantum**.
   The **energy carried** by one of these **wave-packets** had to be:

$$E = hf = \frac{hc}{\lambda}$$

where h = Planck's constant = 6.63×10^{-34} Js, f = frequency (Hz),
λ = wavelength (m) and c = speed of light in a vacuum = 3.00×10^{8} ms^{-1}

2) So, the **higher** the **frequency** of the electromagnetic radiation, the more **energy** its wave-packets carry.
3) **Einstein** went **further** by suggesting that **EM waves** (and the energy they carry) can only **exist** in discrete packets. He called these wave-packets **photons**.
4) He believed that a photon acts as a **particle**, and will either transfer **all** or **none** of its energy when interacting with another particle, like an electron.

Photon Energies are Usually Given in **Electronvolts**

1) The **energies involved** when you're talking about photons are **so tiny** that it makes sense to use a more **appropriate unit** than the **joule**. Bring on the **electronvolt** ...
2) When you **accelerate** an electron between two electrodes, it transfers some electrical potential energy (eV) into kinetic energy.

$$eV = \frac{1}{2}mv^2$$

e is the charge on an electron: 1.6×10^{-19} C.

3) An electronvolt is defined as: The **kinetic energy gained** by an **electron** when it is **accelerated** through a **potential difference** of **1 volt**.
4) So 1 electron volt = $e \times V = 1.6 \times 10^{-19}$ C $\times$ 1 JC^{-1}. ⟹ $1 \text{ eV} = 1.6 \times 10^{-19}$ J

Light — Wave or Photon

Photons *are Released from* ***Electrons*** *in* ***Atoms***

1) **Electrons** in an **atom** can **only exist** in certain **well-defined energy levels**. Each level is given a **number**, with **n = 1** representing the **ground state**.
2) Electrons can **move down** an energy level by **emitting** a **photon**.
3) Since these **transitions** are between **definite energy levels**, the **energy** of **each photon** emitted can **only** take a **certain allowed value**.
4) The diagram on the right shows the **energy levels** for **atomic hydrogen**.
5) The **energy** carried by each **photon** is **equal** to the **difference in energies** between the **two levels**. The equation below shows a **transition** between levels **n = 2** and **n = 1**:

$$\Delta E = E_2 - E_1 = hf = \frac{hc}{\lambda}$$

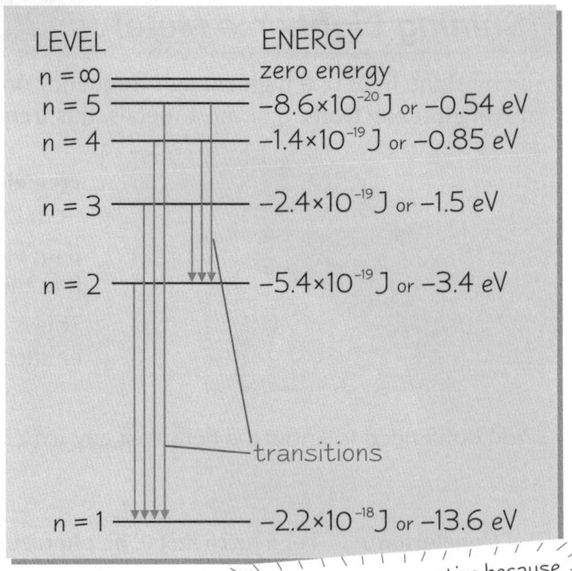

The energies are negative because of how "zero energy" is defined.

Hot Gases *Produce* ***Line Emission Spectra***

1) If you heat a gas to a high temperature, many of its electrons move to higher energy levels.
2) As they fall back to the ground state, these electrons emit energy as photons.
3) If you **split** the light from a **hot gas** with a **prism** or a **diffraction grating** (see pages 54-55), you get a **line spectrum**. A line spectrum is seen as a **series** of **bright lines** against a **black background**.
4) Each **line** corresponds to a **particular wavelength** of light **emitted** by the source. Since only **certain photon energies** are **allowed**, you only see the **corresponding wavelengths**.

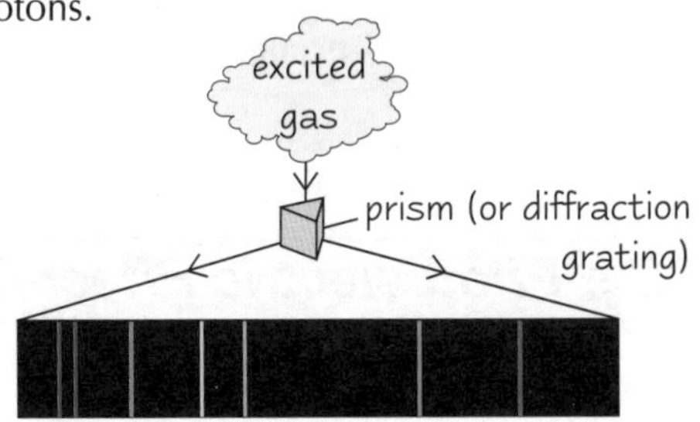

Practice Questions

Q1 Give two different ways to describe the nature of light.

Q2 Write down the two formulas you can use to find the energy of a photon.

Q3 What is an electronvolt? What is 1 eV in joules?

Exam Question

Q1 An electron is accelerated through a potential difference of 12.1 V.

(a) How much kinetic energy has it gained in (i) eV and (ii) joules? [2 marks]

(b) This electron hits a hydrogen atom and excites it.

(i) Explain what is meant by excitation. [1 mark]

(ii) Using the energy values on the right, work out to which energy level the electron from the hydrogen atom is excited. [1 mark]

(iii) Calculate the energies of the three photons that might be emitted as the electron returns to its ground state. [3 marks]

n = 5 — − 0.54 eV
n = 4 — − 0.85 eV
n = 3 — − 1.5 eV
n = 2 — − 3.4 eV
n = 1 — − 13.6 eV

I can honestly say I've never got so excited that I've produced light...

This is heavy stuff, it really is. Quite interesting though, as I was just saying to Dom a moment ago. He's doing a psychology book. Psychology's probably quite interesting too — and easier. But it won't help you become a physicist.

The Photoelectric Effect

The photoelectric effect was one of the original troublemakers in the light-is-it-a-wave-or-a-particle problem...

Shining Light on a Metal can Release Electrons

If you shine **light** of a **high enough frequency** onto the **surface of a metal**, it will **emit electrons**. For **most** metals, this **frequency** falls in the **U.V.** range.

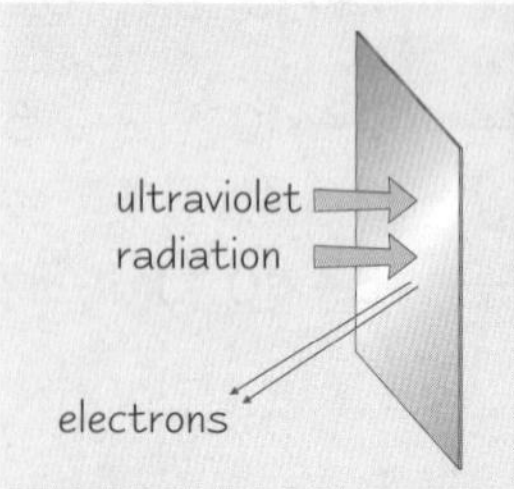

1) **Free electrons** on the **surface** of the metal **absorb energy** from the light, making them **vibrate**.
2) If an electron **absorbs enough** energy, the **bonds** holding it to the metal **break** and the electron is **released**.
3) This is called the **photoelectric effect** and the electrons emitted are called **photoelectrons**.

You don't need to know the details of any experiments on this — you just need to learn the three main conclusions:

Conclusion 1	For a given metal, **no photoelectrons are emitted** if the radiation has a frequency **below** a certain value — called the **threshold frequency**.
Conclusion 2	The photoelectrons are emitted with a variety of kinetic energies ranging from zero to some maximum value. This value of **maximum kinetic energy** increases with the **frequency** of the radiation, and is **unaffected** by the **intensity** of the radiation.
Conclusion 3	The **number** of photoelectrons emitted per second is **proportional** to the **intensity** of the radiation.

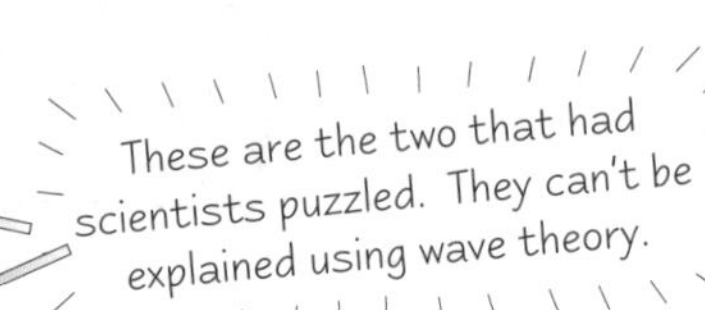

The Photoelectric Effect Couldn't be Explained by Wave Theory

According to wave theory:

1) For a particular frequency of light, the **energy** carried is **proportional** to the **intensity** of the beam.
2) The energy carried by the light would be **spread evenly** over the wavefront.
3) **Each** free electron on the surface of the metal would gain a **bit of energy** from each incoming wave.
4) Gradually, each electron would gain **enough energy** to leave the metal.

SO... If the light had a **lower frequency** (i.e. was carrying less energy) it would take **longer** for the electrons to gain enough energy — but it would happen eventually. There is **no explanation** for the **threshold frequency**.

The **higher the intensity** of the wave, the **more energy** it should transfer to each electron — the kinetic energy should increase with **intensity**. There's **no explanation** for the **kinetic energy** depending only on the **frequency**.

The Photon Model Explained the Photoelectric Effect Nicely

According to the photon model (see page 70)**:**

1) When light hits its surface, the metal is **bombarded** by photons.
2) If one of these photons **collides** with a free electron, the electron will gain energy equal to ***hf***.

Before an electron can **leave** the surface of the metal, it needs enough energy to **break the bonds holding it there**. This energy is called the **work function energy** (symbol ϕ) and its **value** depends on the **metal**.

The Photoelectric Effect

It Explains the Threshold Frequency...

1) If the energy **gained** from the photon is **greater** than the **work function energy**, the electron can be **emitted.**
2) If it **isn't**, the electron will just **shake about a bit**, then release the energy as another photon. The metal will heat up, but **no electrons** will be emitted.
3) Since for **electrons** to be released, $hf \geq \phi$, the **threshold frequency** must be:

$$f = \frac{\phi}{h}$$

In theory, if a second photon hit an electron before it released the energy from the first, it could gain enough to leave the metal. This would have to happen very quickly though. An electron releases any excess energy after about 10^{-8} s. That's 0.000 000 01 s — safe to say, the chances of that happening are pretty slim.

... and the Maximum Kinetic Energy

1) The **energy transferred** to an electron is **hf**.
2) The **kinetic energy** it will be carrying when it **leaves** the metal will be hf **minus** any energy it's **lost** on the way out (there are loads of ways it can do that, which explains the **range** of energies).
3) The **minimum** amount of energy it can lose is the **work function energy**, so the **maximum kinetic energy** is given by the equation:

$$hf = \frac{1}{2}mv_{max}^{2} + \phi$$

4) The **kinetic energy** of the electrons is **independent of the intensity**, because they can **only absorb one photon** at a time.

Practice Questions

Q1 Describe an experiment that demonstrates the photoelectric effect.

Q2 What is meant by the threshold frequency?

Q3 Write down the equation that relates the work function of a metal and the threshold frequency.

Q4 Write an equation that relates the maximum kinetic energy of a photoelectron released from a metal surface and the frequency of the incident light on the surface.

Exam Questions

Q1 The work function of calcium is 2.9 eV.
The threshold frequency of radiation needed for the photoelectric effect to take place is
A 6.5×10^{14} Hz **B** 7.3×10^{12} Hz **C** 7.12 MHz **D** 7.0×10^{14} Hz [1 mark]

Q2 The surface of a copper plate is illuminated with monochromatic ultraviolet light, with a frequency of 2.0×10^{15} Hz.
The work function for copper is 4.7 eV.
(a) Find the energy in eV carried by one ultraviolet photon. [3 marks]
(b) Find the maximum kinetic energy of a photoelectron emitted from the copper surface. [2 marks]

Q3 Explain why the photoelectric effect only occurs after the incident light has reached a certain frequency. [2 marks]

I'm so glad we got that all cleared up...

Well, that's about as hard as it gets at AS. The most important bits here are why wave theory doesn't explain the phenomenon, and why the photon theory does. A good way to learn conceptual stuff like this is to try to explain it to someone else. You'll get the formulas in your handy data book, but it's probably a good idea to learn them too...

Light and Society

Don't worry if you're feeling a bit baffled by the whole 'wave-particle duality' problem — I had to read those pages 14 times before they made any sense. The stuff on these two pages should be easier — it's all about how we can use light.

Solar Cells Convert Solar Energy into Electrical Energy

A solar cell on a calculator

1) You've probably heard of **solar cells** — either from fiddling with your **calculator**, from your **GCSEs**, or from all the people talking about finding green **alternatives to fossil fuels**.
2) **Solar cells** are useful because they **convert** the **unlimited** (hopefully) **free energy** from the **Sun** into **electrical energy** which we can use. And importantly, they do this **without emitting** any nasty **greenhouse gases**.
3) But could solar cells really meet **all** our **energy needs** — or are they too **expensive** and **inefficient**? Scientists need to **find answers** to questions like this if we're going to tackle the problem of **greenhouse gases** and **climate change**.

Radiation Flux is Power Per Unit Area

Solar cells need **energy** from **sunlight** to make **electricity** (with me so far?) — there are **two** ways to **increase** the amount of **sunlight** falling on a solar cell:

1) Increase the **power** of the light
2) Increase the **surface area** of the cell — either by physically increasing the surface area of the cell (well duh...), or **angling** the cell so that a larger amount of its surface **faces** the Sun.

You can't just ask the Sun to up its power — so you have to face your solar cell towards the Sun in an area with stronger sunlight to increase the power.

For example, a **small** solar cell in **strong** sunlight could receive the same amount of light as a **larger** cell in **weak** sunlight.

The **amount of light** falling on an area **facing** (at right angles to) the Sun is called the **radiation flux**.
It's found by dividing the power of the light by the area:

$$\textbf{Radiation flux}\ (Wm^{-2}) = \frac{\textbf{Power}\ (W)}{\textbf{Area}\ (m^2)}$$

Efficiency is the Ratio of Useful Energy Output to Total Energy Input

1) **Efficiency** is one of those words we use all the time, but it has a **specific meaning** in Physics. It's a measure of how well a **device** converts the **energy** you put **in**, into the energy you **want** it to give **out**.
2) So for a **solar cell**, the efficiency is a measure of how well it **converts** energy from **sunlight** into **electrical energy**.
3) You can also calculate the **efficiency** of a device using **power**. Power is **proportional** to energy (see pages 23 and 62), so you get the **same answer** whichever you use. Don't mix them up though — you have to use energy **or** power.
4) There are **two equations** to find the **efficiency** of a device (but they're almost the same, so don't panic):

$$\textbf{Efficiency} = \frac{\textbf{useful output energy}\ (J)}{\textbf{total input energy}\ (J)}$$

$$\textbf{Efficiency} = \frac{\textbf{useful output power}\ (W)}{\textbf{total input power}\ (W)}$$

Example A solar panel measuring 2.5 m^2 receives 980 Wm^{-2} of sunlight. It outputs 20.58 kJ of electrical energy in 1 minute. Calculate the efficiency of the solar cell.

To calculate **efficiency**, you need either the **useful energy output** and **total energy input**, or the **useful power output** and **total power input**.

You can find the **power input** by rearranging the **radiation flux equation:** Power = radiation flux × area.
Input power = 980 × 2.5 = **2450 W**

The **useful output power** is found by dividing the useful output energy by the time taken ($P = \frac{E}{t}$).
Useful output power = $(20.58 \times 10^3) \div (1 \times 60)$ = **343 W.**

Now you can calculate the efficiency. **Efficiency** = $\frac{343}{2450}$ = **0.14**, so the cell is **14% efficient.**

Light and Society

Solar Cells are *Initially Expensive* and *Inefficient*

So, will we **replace** all our **greenhouse-gas-belching power stations** with **solar cells**? The simple answer is that no one knows (unless they've got a crystal ball) — what you have to do is give reasons **for** and **against** replacing the current energy sources with solar cells.

Three reasons **for** replacing energy sources with **solar cells**:

1) The **energy input is free** — it costs money to extract coal, gas and oil, but sunlight doesn't cost a penny.
2) The **energy is unlimited** — fossil fuels will run out one day, but the Sun will keep on shining (if it does stop, we'll all die anyway — a cheery thought for you there).
3) Solar cells are **non-polluting** — aside from the pollution created during manufacture, of course.

Three reasons **against** replacing energy sources with **solar cells**:

1) Solar cells are very **expensive to manufacture** — setting up power stations isn't cheap either, but they give out an awful lot more power for your money.
2) Solar cells are **inefficient** — most solar cells are between 14% and 19% efficient, so the amount of electricity each one can generate is limited.
3) **Output** from solar cells **depends on the weather** — if the Sun is shining brightly, solar cells generate lots of electricity, but if it's not (or it's night) they won't generate as much.

Solar Panels are Used to *Power Remote Sensors*

One area where **solar panels** already prove **useful** is on **space probes** that carry out **remote sensing**. Space probes cannot be **refuelled** easily, so need a source of energy that's always available to them — like **solar energy**.

Remote sensing is really useful because it allows scientists to study areas that would be **difficult** or **dangerous** to go to. It can also be **faster** and **cheaper** than sending people, and a satellite can record data for a **long time** without getting bored, sick or tired. What's more, remote sensing doesn't **disturb the area** being studied, so it's unlikely to influence the data.

Practice Questions

Q1 What is radiation flux? What is the equation for it?

Q2 What are the two equations for efficiency? What is the unit of efficiency?

Q3 Give three reasons for and three reasons against replacing our existing energy sources with solar cells.

Q4 Explain why remote sensing is useful.

Exam Question

Q1 A space probe is powered by two solar panels, each measuring 14 m by 2 m.
The solar panels receive 67.2 kJ of solar energy per second and have a total power output of 12 kW.

(a) What is the radiation flux reaching the solar panels? [3 marks]

(b) Calculate the efficiency of the solar panels. [2 marks]

(c) Describe three benefits of using remote sensing. [3 marks]

Don't look now, but... it's the ENDOFTHESECTION — YAY...

These two pages should please everybody — there are some cold, hard equations, some warm, fuzzy discussion and a hefty dose of real life — what more could you want. Practice questions? Guess what — there's some of those too. Do you know what's sad though? It's the end of the section and almost the end of the book — just a couple of pages to go.

Error Analysis

Science is all about getting good evidence to test your theories... and part of that is knowing how good the results from an experiment are. Physicists always have to include the uncertainty in a result, so you can see the range the actual value probably lies within. Dealing with error and uncertainty is an important skill, so those pesky examiners like to sneak in a couple of questions about it... but if you know your stuff you can get some easy marks.

Nothing is Certain

1) **Every** measurement you take has an **experimental uncertainty**. Say you've done something outrageous like measure the length of a piece of wire with a centimetre ruler. You might think you've measured its length as 30 cm, but at **best** you've probably measured it to be 30 ± **0.5** cm. And that's without taking into account any other errors that might be in your measurement...
2) The ± bit gives you the **range** in which the **true** length (the one you'd really like to know) probably lies — 30 ± 0.5 cm tells you the true length is very likely to lie in the range of 29.5 to 30.5 cm.
3) The smaller the uncertainty, the nearer your value must be to the true value, so the more **accurate** your result.
4) There are **two types** of **error** that cause experimental uncertainty:

Random errors

1) No matter how hard you try, you **can't get rid** of random errors.
2) They can just be down to **noise** (p.72), or that you're measuring a **random process** such as nuclear radiation emission.
3) You get random error in **any** measurement. If you measured the length of a wire 20 times, the chances are you'd get a **slightly different** value each time, e.g. due to your head being in a slightly different position when reading the scale.
4) It could be that you just can't keep controlled variables **exactly** the same throughout the experiment.
5) Or it could just be the wind was blowing in the wrong direction at the time...

Systematic errors

1) You get systematic errors not because you've made a mistake in a measurement — but because of the **apparatus** you're using, or your experimental method. E.g. using an inaccurate clock.
2) The problem is often that you **don't know they're there**. You've got to spot them first to have any chance of correcting for them.
3) Systematic errors usually **shift** all of your results to be too high or too low by the **same amount**. They're annoying, but there are things you can do to reduce them if you manage to spot them...

Lorraine thought getting an uncertainty of ± 0.1 A deserved a victory dance.

You Need to Know How to Improve Measurements

There are a few different ways you can **reduce** the uncertainty in your results:

Repeating measurements — by repeating a measurement **several times** and **averaging**, you reduce the **random uncertainty** in your result. The **more** measurements you average over, the **less error** you're likely to have.

Use higher precision apparatus — the **more precisely** you can measure something, the **less random error** there is in the measurement. So if you use more precise equipment — e.g. swapping a millimetre ruler for a micrometer to measure the diameter of a wire — you can instantly cut down the **random error** in your experiment.

Calibration — you can calibrate your apparatus by measuring a **known value**. If there's a **difference** between the **measured** and **known** value, you can use this to **correct** the inaccuracy of the apparatus, and so reduce your **systematic error**.

You can Calculate the Percentage Uncertainty in a Measurement

1) You might get asked to work out the percentage uncertainty in a measurement.
2) It's just working out a percentage, so nothing too tricky. It's just that sometimes you can get **the fear** as soon as you see the word uncertainty... but just keep your cool and you can pick up some easy marks.

Example

Tom finds the resistance of a filament lamp to be **5.0 ± 0.4 Ω**.

The percentage uncertainty in the resistance measured $= \frac{0.4}{5.0} \times 100 = \mathbf{8\%}$

Error Analysis

You can Estimate Values by Averaging

You might be given a graph of information showing the results for many **repetitions** of the **same** experiment, and asked to estimate the true value and give an uncertainty in that value. Yuk. Here's how to go about it:

1) Estimate the true value by **averaging** the results you've been given. (Make sure you state whatever average it is you take, otherwise you might not get the mark.)
2) To get the uncertainty, you just need to look how far away from your average value the maximum and minimum values in the graph you've been given are.

Example — Estimating the resistance of a component

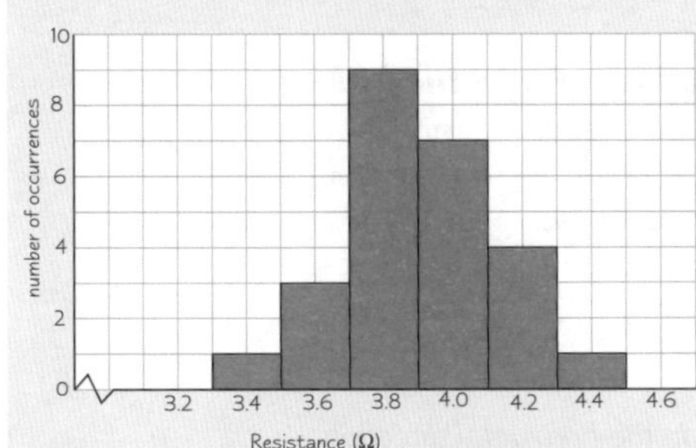

A class measure the resistance of a component and record their results on the bar chart shown. Estimate the resistance of the component, giving a suitable range of uncertainty in your answer.

There were 25 measurements, so taking the **mean**:

$$\frac{(3.4+(3.6\times3)+(3.8\times9)+(4.0\times7)+(4.2\times4)+4.4)}{25}=\frac{97.6}{25}=3.90\ (3\text{ s.f.})$$

The maximum value found was 4.4 Ω, the minimum value was 3.4. Both values are both about 0.5 Ω from the average value, so the answer is **3.9 ± 0.5 Ω**.

Error Bars to Show Uncertainty on a Graph

1) Most of the time in science, you work out the uncertainty in your **final result** using the uncertainty in **each measurement** you make.
2) When you're plotting a graph, you show the uncertainty in a value by using **error bars** to show the range the point is likely to lie in.
3) You probably won't get asked to **plot** any error bars (phew...) — but you might need to **read off** a graph that has them.

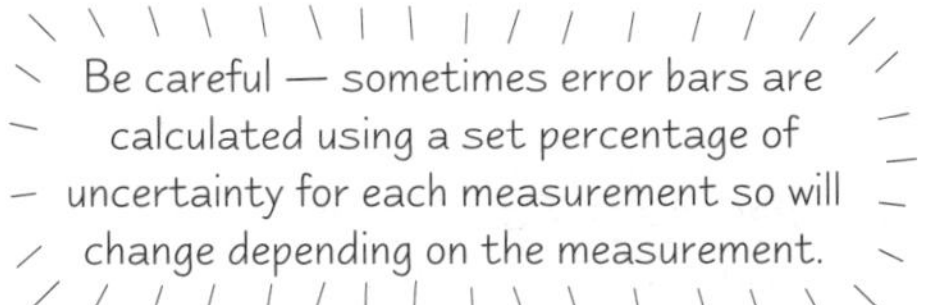

Be careful — sometimes error bars are calculated using a set percentage of uncertainty for each measurement so will change depending on the measurement.

Example

Use the graph below to find the error in measuring the extension of material X.

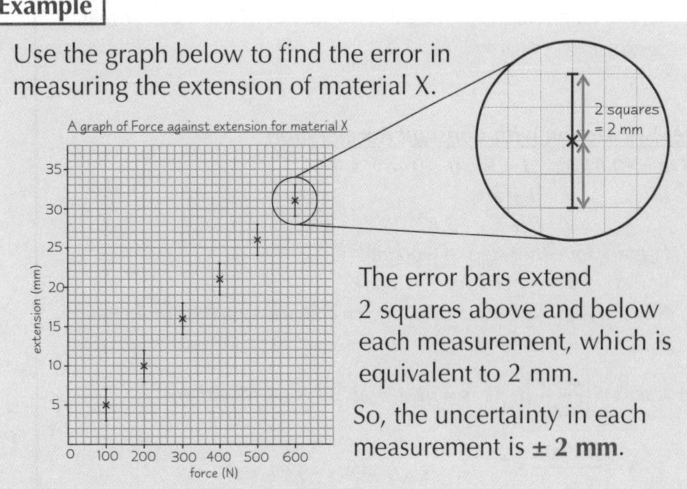

The error bars extend 2 squares above and below each measurement, which is equivalent to 2 mm.

So, the uncertainty in each measurement is **± 2 mm.**

You can Estimate the Uncertainty of the Graph's Gradient

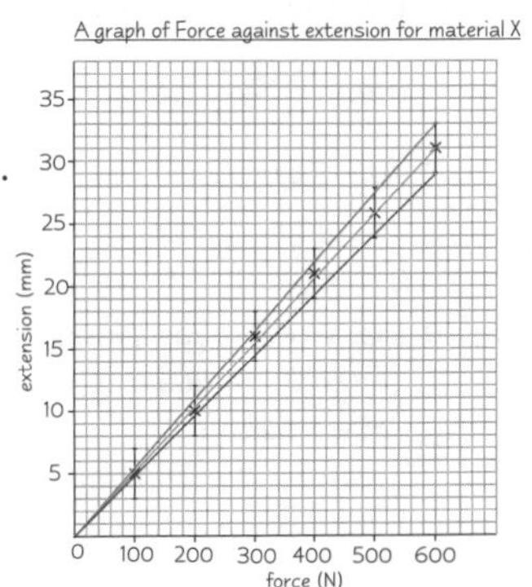

1) Normally when you draw a graph you'll want to find the gradient or intercept. E.g. for a force-extension graph, the gradient's $1/k$, the stiffness constant of the material.
2) To find the value of k, you draw a nice line of best fit on the graph and calculate your answer from that. No problem there.
3) You can then draw the **maximum** and **minimum** slopes possible for the data through **all** of the error bars. By calculating the value of the gradient (or intercept) for these slopes, you can find maximum and minimum values the true answer is likely to lie between. And that's the **uncertainty** in your answer.

Random error in your favour — collect £200...

These pages should give you a fair idea of how to deal with errors... which are rather annoyingly in everything. Even if you're lucky enough to not get tested on this sort of thing in the exam, it's really useful to know for your lab coursework.

Answers

Unit 1: Section 1 — Mechanics

Page 5 — Scalars and Vectors

1) Start by drawing a diagram:

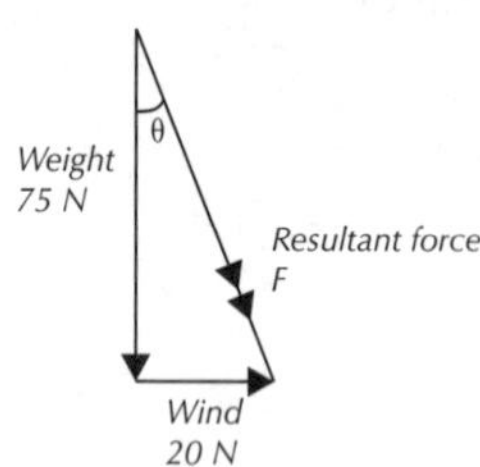

$F^2 = 20^2 + 75^2 = 6025$
So $F = 77.6$ N
$\tan q = 20 / 75 = 0.267$
So $q = 14.9°$
B 14.9° [1 mark]
Make sure you know which angle you're finding — and label it on your diagram.

2) Again, start by drawing a diagram:

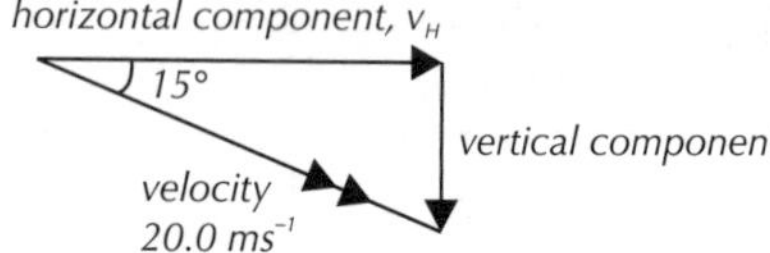

horizontal component $v_H = 20 \cos 15° = 19.3$ ms^{-1} [1 mark]
vertical component $v_V = 20 \sin 15° = 5.2$ ms^{-1} downwards [1 mark]
Always draw a diagram.

Page 7 — Motion with Constant Acceleration

1)a) $\mathbf{a} = -9.81$ ms^{-2}, $\mathbf{t} = 5$ s, $\mathbf{u} = 0$ ms^{-1}, $\mathbf{v} = ?$
use : $\mathbf{v} = \mathbf{u} + \mathbf{at}$
$\mathbf{v} = 0 + 5 \times -9.81$
[1 mark for either step of working]
$\mathbf{v} = -49.05$ ms^{-1} [1 mark]
NB: It's negative because she's falling downwards and we took upwards as the positive direction.

b) Use: $\mathbf{s} = \left(\frac{\mathbf{u}+\mathbf{v}}{2}\right)\mathbf{t}$ or $\mathbf{s} = \mathbf{ut} + \frac{1}{2}\mathbf{at}^2$ [1 mark for either]

$\mathbf{s} = \frac{-49.05}{2} \times 5$ $\quad$ $\mathbf{s} = 0 + \frac{1}{2} \times -9.81 \times 5^2$
$\mathbf{s} = -122.625$ m $\quad$ $\mathbf{s} = -122.625$ m
So she fell 122.625 m [1 mark for answer]

2)a) $\mathbf{v} = 0$ ms^{-1}, $\mathbf{t} = 3.2$ s, $\mathbf{s} = 40$ m, $\mathbf{u} = ?$

use: $\mathbf{s} = \left(\frac{\mathbf{u}+\mathbf{v}}{2}\right)\mathbf{t}$ [1 mark]

$40 = 3.2\mathbf{u} \div 2$

$\mathbf{u} = \frac{80}{3.2} = 25$ ms^{-1} [1 mark]

b) use: $\mathbf{v}^2 = \mathbf{u}^2 + 2\mathbf{as}$ [1 mark]
$0 = 25^2 + 80\mathbf{a}$
$-80\mathbf{a} = 625$
$\mathbf{a} = -7.8$ ms^{-2} [1 mark]

3)a) Take upstream as negative: $\mathbf{v} = 5$ ms^{-1}, $\mathbf{a} = 6$ ms^{-2}, $\mathbf{s} = 1.2$ m, $\mathbf{u} = ?$
use: $\mathbf{v}^2 = \mathbf{u}^2 + 2\mathbf{as}$ [1 mark]
$5^2 = \mathbf{u}^2 + 2 \times 6 \times 1.2$
$\mathbf{u}^2 = 25 - 14.4 = 10.6$
$\mathbf{u} = -3.26$ ms^{-1} [1 mark]

b) From furthest point: $\mathbf{u} = 0$ ms^{-1}, $\mathbf{a} = 6$ ms^{-2}, $\mathbf{v} = 5$ ms^{-1}, $\mathbf{s} = ?$
use: $\mathbf{v}^2 = \mathbf{u}^2 + 2\mathbf{as}$ [1 mark]
$5^2 = 0 + 2 \times 6 \times \mathbf{s}$
$\mathbf{s} = 25 \div 12 = 2.08$ m [1 mark]

Page 9 — Free Fall and Projectile Motion

1)a) You only need worry about the stone's vertical motion.
$\mathbf{u} = 0$ ms^{-1}, $\mathbf{s} = -560$ m, $\mathbf{a} = -\mathbf{g} = -9.81$ ms^{-2}, $\mathbf{t} = ?$
You need to find $\mathbf{t}$, so use: $\mathbf{s} = \mathbf{ut} + \frac{1}{2}\mathbf{at}^2$ [1 mark]
$-560 = 0 + \frac{1}{2} \times -9.81 \times \mathbf{t}^2$

$\mathbf{t} = \sqrt{\frac{2 \times (-560)}{-9.81}} = 10.7\text{s (1 d.p.)} \approx 11\text{ s}$ [1 mark]

b) You know that in the horizontal direction:
$\mathbf{v} = 20$ m/s, $\mathbf{t} = 10.7$ s, $\mathbf{a} = 0$, $\mathbf{s} = ?$

So use velocity $= \frac{\text{distance}}{\text{time}}$, $\mathbf{v} = \frac{\mathbf{s}}{\mathbf{t}}$ [1 mark]

$\mathbf{s} = \mathbf{v} \times \mathbf{t} = 20 \times 10.7 = 214$ m (to the nearest metre) [1 mark]

2) You know that for the arrow's vertical motion (taking upwards as the positive direction):
$\mathbf{a} = -9.81$ ms^{-2}, $\mathbf{u} = 30$ ms^{-1} and the arrow will be at its highest point just before it starts falling back towards the ground, so $\mathbf{v} = 0$ m/s.
$\mathbf{s}$ = the distance travelled from the arrow's firing point
So use $\mathbf{v}^2 = \mathbf{u}^2 + 2\mathbf{as}$ [1 mark]
$0 = 30^2 + 2 \times -9.81 \times \mathbf{s}$

$900 = 2 \times 9.81\mathbf{s}$

$\mathbf{s} = \frac{900}{2 \times 9.81} = 45.9$ m [1 mark]

So the maximum distance reached from the ground = 45.9 + 1 = 47 m (to the nearest metre). [1 mark]

Page 11 — Displacement-Time Graphs

1) Split graph into four sections:

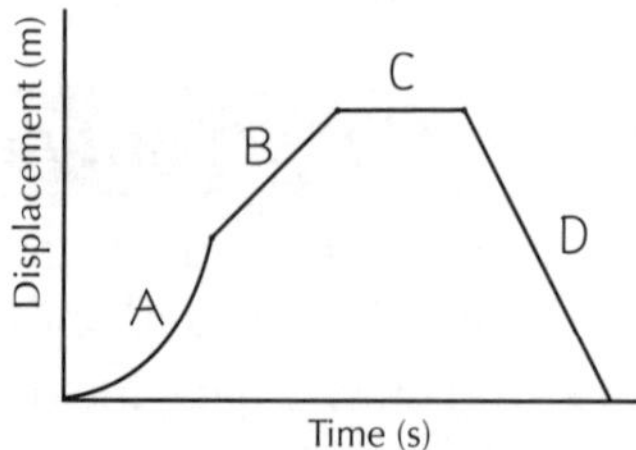

A: acceleration [1 mark]
B: constant velocity [1 mark]
C: stationary [1 mark]
D: constant velocity in opposite direction to A and B [1 mark]

Answers

2)a)

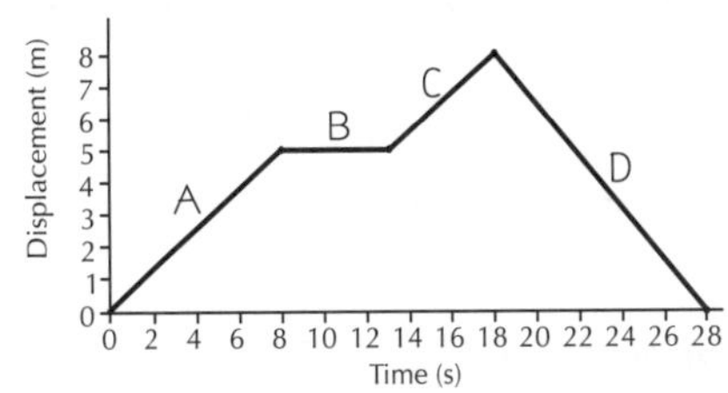

[4 marks — 1 mark for each section correctly drawn]

b) At A: $\mathbf{v} = \frac{\text{displacement}}{\text{time}} = \frac{5}{8} = 0.625\ ms^{-1}$

At B: $\mathbf{v} = 0$

At C: $\mathbf{v} = \frac{\text{displacement}}{\text{time}} = \frac{3}{5} = 0.6\ ms^{-1}$

At D: $\mathbf{v} = \frac{\text{displacement}}{\text{time}} = \frac{-8}{10} = -0.8\ ms^{-1}$

[2 marks for all correct or just 1 mark for 2 or 3 correct]

Page 13 — Velocity-Time Graphs

1)a)

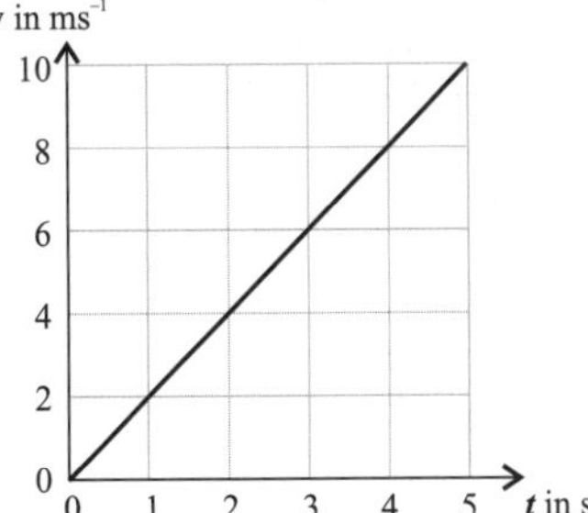

[1 mark for a straight line graph starting at 0,0, 1 mark for a graph with a gradient of 2 ms^{-2}]

b) use $\mathbf{s} = \mathbf{ut} + \frac{1}{2}\mathbf{at}^2$ [1 mark]

$\mathbf{t} = 1, \mathbf{s} = 1$

$\mathbf{t} = 2, \mathbf{s} = 4$

$\mathbf{t} = 3, \mathbf{s} = 9$

$\mathbf{t} = 4, \mathbf{s} = 16$

$\mathbf{t} = 5, \mathbf{s} = 25$

[2 marks for all correct or 1 mark for at least 3 pairs of values right]

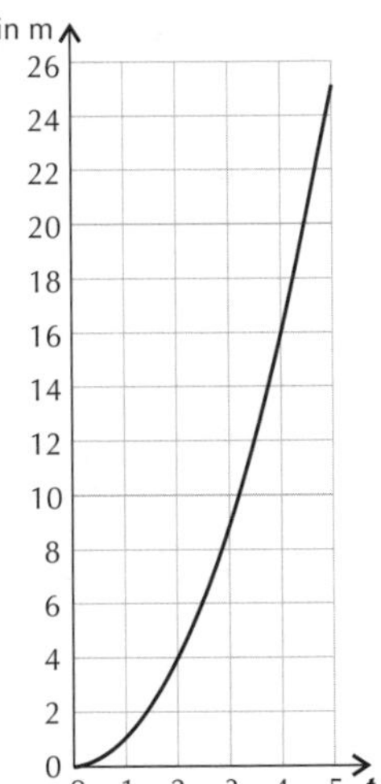

[2 marks]

c) E.g. another way to calculate displacement is to find the area under the velocity-time graph. [1 mark]

E.g. total displacement = $\frac{1}{2} \times 5 \times 10 = 25$ m [1 mark]

Page 15 — Mass, Weight and Centre of Gravity

1) a) Density is a measure of 'compactness' of a material — its mass per unit volume. [1 mark]

b) $\rho = \frac{\mathbf{m}}{\mathbf{V}}$ [1 mark]

V of cylinder = $\pi \mathbf{r}^2\mathbf{h} = \pi \times 4^2 \times 6 = 301.6\ cm^3$ [1 mark]

$\rho = 820 \div 301.6 = 2.72\ g\,cm^{-3}$ [1 mark]

c) $\mathbf{V} = 5 \times 5 \times 5 = 125\ cm^3$

$\mathbf{m} = \rho \times \mathbf{V} = 2.7 \times 125 = 340$ g [1 mark]

2) Experiment:

Hang the object freely from a point. Hang a plumb bob from the same point, and use it to draw a vertical line down the object. [1 mark]

Repeat for a different point and find the point of intersection. [1 mark]

The centre of gravity is halfway through the thickness of the object (by symmetry) at the point of intersection [1 mark].

Identifying and reducing error, e.g.:

Source: the object and/or plumb line might move slightly while you're drawing the vertical line [1 mark]

Reduced by: hang the object from a third point to confirm the position of the point of intersection [1 mark].

Page 17 — Forces

1)

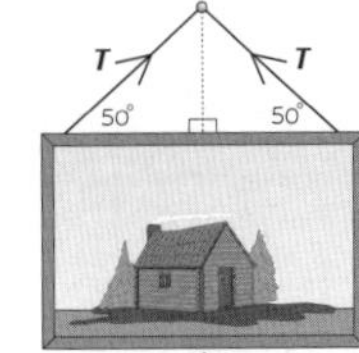

Weight = vertical component of tension × 2

$8 \times 9.81 = 2\mathbf{T} \sin 50°$

$78.48 = 0.766 \times 2\mathbf{T}$

$102.45 = 2\mathbf{T}$

$\mathbf{T} = 51.2$ N

B 51.2 N [1 mark]

2)

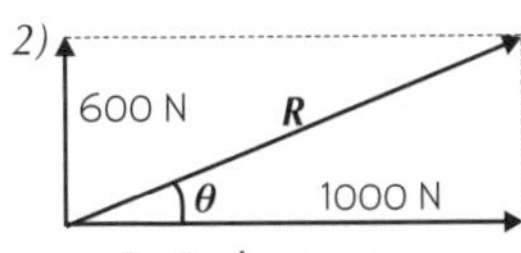

By Pythagoras:

$\mathbf{R} = \sqrt{1000^2 + 600^2} = 1166$ N [1 mark]

$\tan \theta = \frac{600}{1000}$, so $\theta = \tan^{-1} 0.6 = 31.0°$ [1 mark]

Page 19 — Newton's Laws of Motion

1)

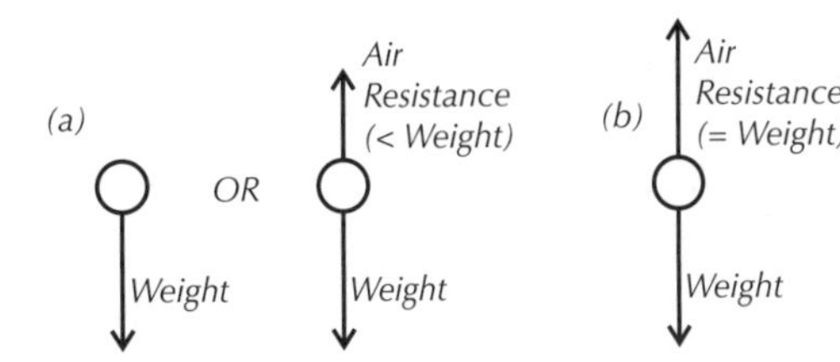

[1 mark for each diagram]

Answers

2)a) *Force perpendicular to river flow = 500 – 100 = 400 N [1 mark]*
Force parallel to river flow = 300 N

Resultant force = $\sqrt{400^2 + 300^2}$ *= 500 N [1 mark]*

b) **a** = **F**/**m** (from **F** = **ma**) *[1 mark] = 500/250 = 2 ms*$^{-2}$ *[1 mark]*

3)a) *The resultant force acting on it [1 mark] and its mass. [1 mark]*

b) *Michael is able to exert a greater force than Tom.*
Michael is lighter than Tom.
[1 mark each for 2 sensible points]

c) *The only force acting on each of them is their weight =* **mg** *[1 mark].*
Since **F** = **ma**, *this gives* **ma** = **mg**, *or* **a** = g *[1 mark]. Their acceleration doesn't depend on their mass — it's the same for both of them — so they reach the water at the same time. [1 mark]*

Page 21 — Mechanics in the Real World

1)a) *Reaction time is 0.5 s, speed is 20 ms*$^{-1}$
s = **vt** *[1 mark] = 20 × 0.5 = 10 m [1 mark]*

b) *Use* **F** = **ma** *to get* **a**: **a** *= –10 000/850 = –11.76 ms*$^{-2}$ *[1 mark]*

Use $v^2 = u^2 + 2as$, *and rearrange to get* $s = \frac{v^2 - u^2}{2a}$

Put in the values:
s *= (0 – 400) ÷ (2 × –11.76) [1 mark] = 17 m [1 mark]*
Remember that a force against the direction of motion is negative.

c) *Total stopping distance = 10 + 17 = 27 m*
She stops 3 m before the cow. [1 mark]

2)a) *Car: use* **v** = **u** + **at** *to get acceleration:*
a *= (0 – 20)/0.1 = –200 ms*$^{-2}$ *[1 mark]*
Use **F** = **ma**:
F *= 900 × –200 = –180 000 N [1 mark]*
Same for dummy:
a *= 0 – 18/0.1 = –180 ms*$^{-2}$ *[1 mark]*
F *= 50 × –180 = –9000 N [1 mark]*

b) *Crumple zones will increase the collision time for the car and dummy;*
this reduces forces on the car and dummy;
the airbag will keep the dummy in its seat;
and increase the collision time further for the dummy;
reducing the force on it.
[3 marks for any three sensible points]

3) i) ii)

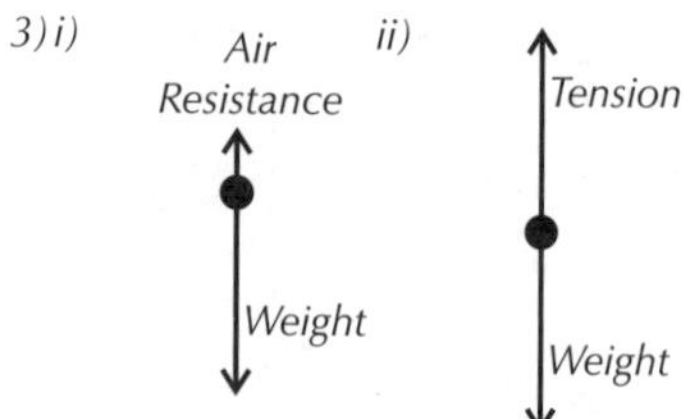

[1 mark for each diagram]

Page 23 — Work and Power

1)

100 cos 40° N
40°
100 N

Force in direction of travel = 100 cos40° = 76.6 N
W = **Fs** *= 76.6 × 1500 = 114 900 J*
A *114 900 J [1 mark]*

2)a) *Use* **W** = **Fs** *[1 mark]*
= 20 × 9.81 × 3 = 588.6 J [1 mark]
Remember that 20 kg is not the force — it's the mass. So you need to multiply it by 9.81 Nkg^{-1} to get the weight.

b) *Use* **P** = **Fv** *[1 mark]*
= 20 × 9.81 × 0.25 = 49.05 W [1 mark]

Page 25 — Conservation of Energy

1)a) *Use* $E_k = \frac{1}{2}mv^2$ *and* $E_p = mgh$ *[1 mark]*
$\frac{1}{2}mv^2 = mgh$
$\frac{1}{2}v^2 = gh$
$v^2 = 2gh$ *= 2 × 9.81 × 2 = 39.24 [1 mark]*
v *= 6.26 ms*$^{-1}$ *[1 mark]*
'No friction' allows you to say that the changes in kinetic and potential energy will be the same.

b) *2 m — no friction means the kinetic energy will all change back into potential energy, so he will rise back up to the same height as he started. [1 mark]*

c) *Put in some more energy by actively 'skating'.*
[1 mark]

2)a) *If there's no air resistance,* $E_k = E_p = mgh$ *[1 mark]*
E_k *= 0.02 × 9.81 × 8 = 1.57 J [1 mark]*

b) *If the ball rebounds to 6.5 m, it has gravitational potential energy:*
$E_p = mgh$ *= 0.02 × 9.81 × 6.5 = 1.28 J [1 mark]*
So 1.57 – 1.28 = 0.29 J is converted to other forms [1 mark]

Unit 1: Section 2 — Materials

Page 27 — Hooke's Law

1)a) *Force is proportional to extension.*
The force is 1.5 times as great, so the extension will also be 1.5 times the original value.
Extension = 1.5 × 4.0 mm = 6.0 mm [1 mark]

b) **F** = **ke** *and so* **k** = **F**/**e** *[1 mark]*
k *= 10 ÷ 4.0 × 10*$^{-3}$ *= 2500 Nm*$^{-1}$ *[1 mark]*
There is one mark for rearranging the equation and another for getting the right numerical answer.

c) *One mark for any sensible point e.g.*
The string now stretches much further for small increases in force.
When the string is loosened it is longer than at the start. [1 mark]

2) *The rubber band does not obey Hooke's law [1 mark] because when the force is doubled from 2.5 N to 5 N, the extension increases by a factor of 2.3. [1 mark]*

Page 29 — Stress and Strain

1)a) *Area =* $\pi d^2/4$ *or* πr^2.
So area = π *× (1 × 10*$^{-3}$*)*^{2}*/4 = 7.85 × 10*$^{-7}$ *m*^{2} *[1 mark]*

b) *Stress = force/area = 300/(7.85 × 10*$^{-7}$*)*
= 3.82 × 10^{8} *Nm*$^{-2}$ *[1 mark]*

c) *Strain = extension/length = 4 × 10*$^{-3}$*/2.00 = 2 × 10*$^{-3}$
[1 mark]

2)a) **F** = **ke** *and so rearranging* **k** = **F**/**e** *[1 mark]*
So **k** *= 50/(3.0 × 10*$^{-3}$*) = 1.67 × 10*^{4} *Nm*$^{-1}$ *[1 mark]*

b) *Elastic strain energy =* $\frac{1}{2}$**Fe**
Giving the elastic strain energy as
½ × 50 × 3 × 10^{-3} *= 7.5 × 10*$^{-2}$ *J [1 mark]*

Answers

3) Elastic strain energy,
$E = \frac{1}{2}ke^2 = \frac{1}{2} \times 40.8 \times 0.05^2 = 0.051$ J
To find maximum speed, assume all this energy is converted to kinetic energy in the ball. $E_{kinetic} = E$
$E = \frac{1}{2}mv^2$, so rearranging, $v^2 = 2E/m$
$v^2 = (2 \times 0.051)/0.012 = 8.5$, so $v = 2.92$ ms^{-1}
B 2.92 ms^{-1} [1 mark]

Page 31 — The Young Modulus

1)a) Cross-sectional area = $\pi d^2/4$ or πr^2.
So the cross-sectional area = $\pi \times (0.6 \times 10^{-3})^2/4$
$= 2.83 \times 10^{-7}$ m^2 [1 mark]
b) Stress = force/area = $80/(2.83 \times 10^{-7})$
$= 2.83 \times 10^8$ Nm^{-2} [1 mark]
c) Strain = extension/length = $3.6 \times 10^{-3}/2.5 = 1.44 \times 10^{-3}$ [1 mark]
d) The Young modulus for steel = stress/strain
$= 2.83 \times 10^8/(1.44 \times 10^{-3}) = 2.0 \times 10^{11}$ Nm^{-2} [1 mark]

2)a) The Young modulus, **E** = stress/strain
and so strain = stress/**E** [1 mark]
Strain on copper = $2.6 \times 10^8/1.3 \times 10^{11} = 2 \times 10^{-3}$
[1 mark]
There's one mark for rearranging the equation and another for using it.
b) Stress = force/area and so area = force/stress
Area of the wire = $100/(2.6 \times 10^8) = 3.85 \times 10^{-7}$ m^2 [1 mark]
c) Strain energy per unit volume = ½ × stress × strain
$= \frac{1}{2} \times 2.6 \times 10^8 \times 2 \times 10^{-3} = 2.6 \times 10^5$ Jm^{-3} [1 mark]
Give the mark if answer is consistent with the value calculated for strain in part a).

Page 33 — Behaviour of Solids

1) The material isn't stiff because it can be easily shaped, which rules out A and D and must be ductile because it keeps its strength when shaped.
C malleable, ductile and tough [1 mark]

2) One mark for any sensible use e.g. a cutting instrument. [1 mark]
One further mark for an explanation relating the use to the properties of hardened steel e.g. because the instrument would be able to cut through surfaces without getting damaged itself.
[1 mark]

3) E.g. The material would need to be stiff [1 mark] so that it would keep its shape and not crush the rider's head when a force was applied to it. [1 mark]
It would also need to be tough [1 mark] so that it could absorb the energy of an impact without breaking. [1 mark]
The material should be lightweight / should have a low density [1 mark] so that it is comfortable for the rider to wear. [1 mark]

Page 35 — Streamlines and Flow

1)a)

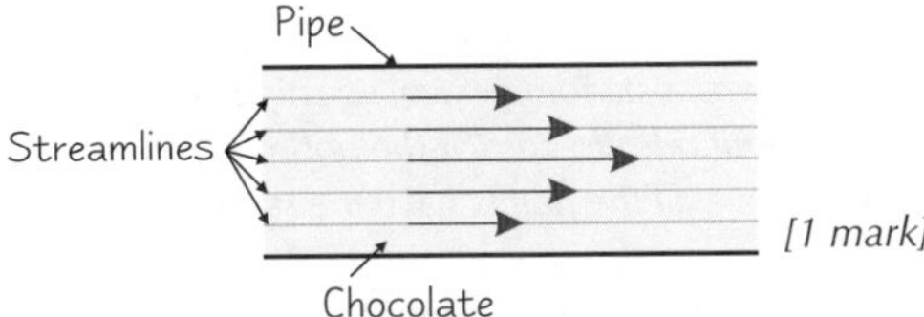

[1 mark]

The chocolate in the pipe is undergoing laminar flow. [1 mark]
This is a flow pattern where all the fluid elements flow in the same direction [1 mark], so all the flowlines are streamlines that run parallel to each another. [1 mark]

b) Chocolate is highly viscous, and so its rate of flow is limited by a large viscous drag force. [1 mark]
This is a frictional force caused by fluid elements in the chocolate moving past each other with different velocities. [1 mark]
c) When the chocolate enters the mixing container, the flow pattern changes to turbulent flow. [1 mark]
The fluid elements within the chocolate get mixed up and the flowlines become unstable. [1 mark]

Page 37 — Viscosity

1)a)

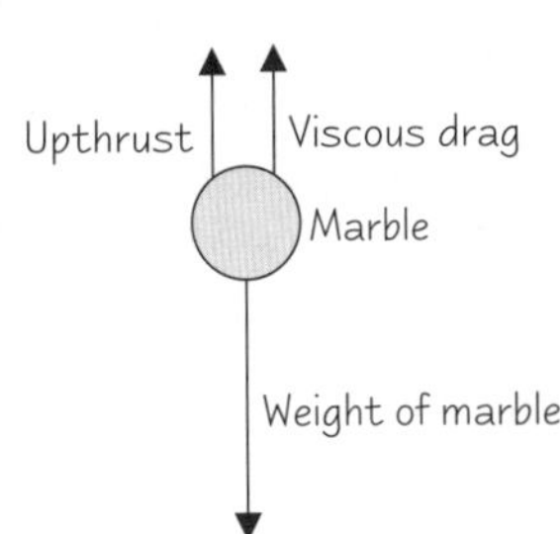

[1 mark for each force correctly drawn and labelled]
b) The resultant force is zero. [1 mark]
c) Weight of marble = mg = $5 \times 10^{-5} \times 9.81$
$= 4.9 \times 10^{-4}$ N [1 mark]
Weight of displaced water = mg
$= 2.1 \times 10^{-5} \times 9.81 = 2.1 \times 10^{-4}$ N
Upthrust = weight of displaced water = 2.1×10^{-4} N [1 mark]
Viscous drag (F) + upthrust – weight of marble = 0 N
[1 mark]
Viscous drag = weight of marble – upthrust
$= 4.9 \times 10^{-4} - 2.1 \times 10^{-4} = 2.8 \times 10^{-4}$ N [1 mark]
Stoke's law states $F = 6\pi\eta rv$.
Rearranging, $v = F \div (6\pi\eta r)$ [1 mark]
$v = 2.8 \times 10^{-4} \div [6 \times \pi \times 0.0011 \times (5 \times 10^{-3})]$
$= 2.7$ ms^{-1} [1 mark]

2) Oil flows more slowly during the night because nights tend to be colder than days [1 mark].
The lower temperature means that the viscosity of the fuel is greater at night [1 mark], which in turn means that its rate of flow is slower than in the day [1 mark].

Unit 2: Section 1 — Waves

Page 39 — The Nature of Waves

1)a) Use $v = \lambda f$ and $f = 1/T$
So $v = \lambda / T$, giving $\lambda = vT$
$\lambda = 3$ ms$^{-1} \times 6$ s $= 18$ m
C 18 m [1 mark]
The vertical movement of the buoy is irrelevant to this part of the question.
b) The trough to peak distance is twice the amplitude, so the amplitude is **C** 0.6 m. [1 mark]

Answers

Page 41 — Longitudinal and Transverse Waves

1) *[This question could equally well be answered using diagrams.] For ordinary light, the EM field vibrates in all planes at right angles to the direction of travel. [1 mark]*
Iceland spar acts as a polariser. [1 mark]
When light is shone through the first disc, it only allows through vibrations in one particular plane, so emerges less bright. [1 mark]
As the two crystals are rotated relative to each other there comes a point when the allowed planes are at right angles to each other. [1 mark] So all the light is blocked. [1 mark]
Try to remember to say that for light and other EM waves it's the electric and magnetic fields that vibrate.

2) *E.g. Polarising filters are used in photography to remove unwanted reflections [1 mark].*
Light is partially polarised when it reflects so putting a polarising filter over the lens at 90 degrees to the plane of polarisation will block most of the reflected light. [1 mark].

Page 43 — Ultrasound Imaging

1)a)

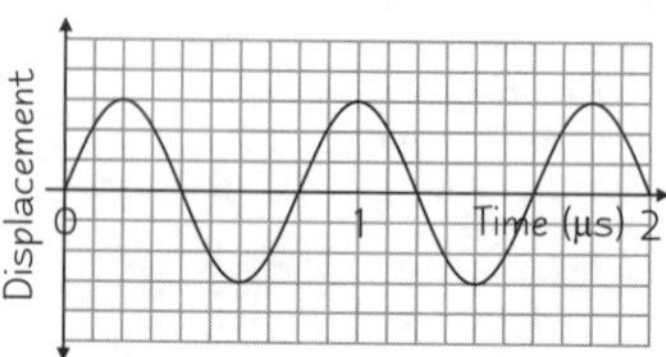

The graph should have a shorter wavelength and lower amplitude than the original. [1 mark]

b)

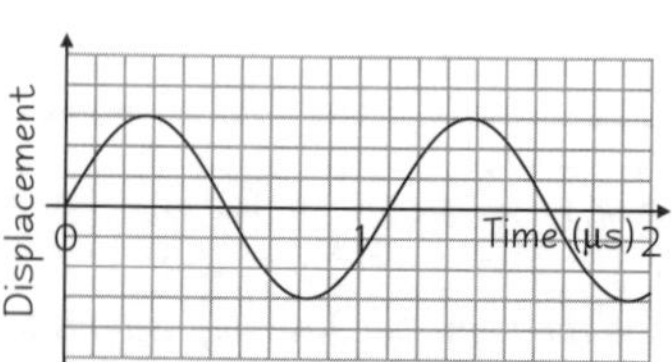

The graph should have a longer wavelength and lower amplitude than the original. [1 mark]

2) *Any two of, e.g. It will be very expensive and the money could be better spent on development in technologies that would have a more immediate benefit. / The trip will have a huge psychological and physiological effect on the astronauts involved. / Space missions have a very high risk of fatality for the astronauts.*
[1 mark for describing an issue, 1 mark for explaining it — to a maximum of 4 marks]

Page 45 — The Electromagnetic Spectrum

1) *At the same speed. [1 mark]*
Both are electromagnetic waves and hence travel at **c** *in a vacuum. [1 mark]*

2)a) *Medical X-rays [1 mark] rely on the fact that X-rays penetrate the body well but are blocked by bone. [1 mark]*
OR
Security scanners at airports [1 mark] rely on the fact that X-rays penetrate suitcases and clothes but are blocked by metal e.g. of a weapon. [1 mark]

b) *The main difference between gamma rays and X-rays is that gamma rays arise from nuclear decay [1 mark] but X-rays are generated when metals are bombarded with electrons. [1 mark]*

3) *Any of: unshielded microwaves, excess heat, damage to eyes from too bright light, sunburn or skin cancer from UV, cancer or eye damage due to ionisation by X-rays or gamma rays.*
[1 mark for the type of EM wave, 1 mark for the danger to health]

Page 47 — Refractive Index

1)a) $\mu_{diamond} = c / v_{diamond} = (3 \times 10^8) / (1.24 \times 10^8) = 2.42$ *[1 mark]*

b) $\mu_{air} \sin i = \mu_{diamond} \sin r$, $\mu_{air} = 1$
So, $\mu_{diamond} = \sin i / \sin r$ *[1 mark]*

$$\sin r = \frac{\sin i}{\mu_{diamond}} = \frac{\sin 50}{2.42} = 0.317$$

$r = 18.5°$ *[1 mark]*
You can assume the refractive index of air is 1, and don't forget to write the degree sign in your answer.

2)a) *When the light is pointing steeply upwards some of it is refracted and some reflected — the beam emerging from the surface is the refracted part. [1 mark]*
However when the beam hits the surface at more than the critical angle (to the normal to the boundary) refraction does not occur. All the beam is totally internally reflected to light the tank, hence its brightness. [1 mark]

b) *The critical angle is 90° – 41.25° = 48.75°. [1 mark]*
$\mu_{water} = 1 / \sin C$
$= 1 / \sin 48.75°$
$= 1 / 0.752 = 1.33$ *[1 mark]*
The question talks about the angle between the light beam and the floor of the aquarium. This angle is 90° minus the incident angle — measured from a normal to the surface of the water.

Page 49 — Superposition and Coherence

1)a) *The frequencies and wavelengths of the two sources must be equal [1 mark] and the phase difference must be constant. [1 mark]*

b) *Interference will only be noticeable if the amplitudes of the two waves are approximately equal. [1 mark]*

2)a) *180° (or 180° + 360n°). [1 mark]*

b) *The displacements and velocities of the two points are equal in size [1 mark] but in opposite directions. [1 mark]*

Page 51 — Standing (Stationary) Waves

1)a)

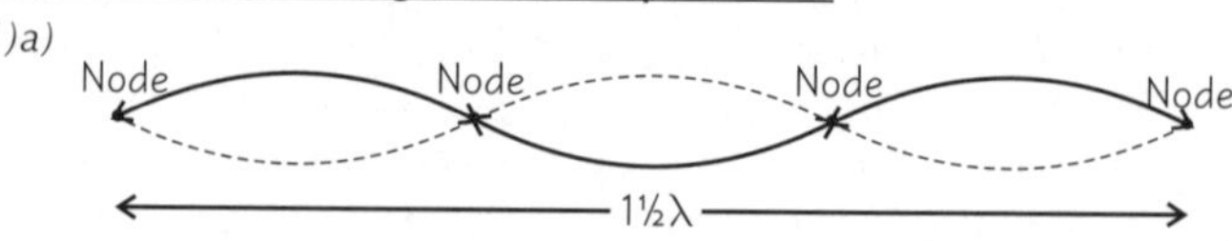

[1 mark for the correct shape, 1 mark for labelling the length]

b) *For a string vibrating at three times the fundamental frequency,*
length = $3\lambda / 2$
$1.2 \text{ m} = 3\lambda / 2$
$\lambda = 0.8 \text{ m}$ *[1 mark]*

c) *When the string forms a standing wave, its amplitude varies from a maximum at the antinodes to zero at the nodes. [1 mark]*
In a progressive wave all the points have the same amplitude. [1 mark]

d) *The displacements in successive antinodes are of equal size [1 mark] but opposite directions. [1 mark]*
Remember that displacement is how "far out" the vibrating particle is at a particular time. Amplitude is the maximum displacement the particle ever reaches.

Answers

Page 53 — Diffraction

1) When a wavefront meets an obstacle, the waves will diffract round the corners of the obstacle. When the obstacle is much bigger than the wavelength, little diffraction occurs. In this case, the mountain is much bigger than the wavelength of short-wave radio. So the "shadow" where you cannot pick up short wave is very long. [1 mark]

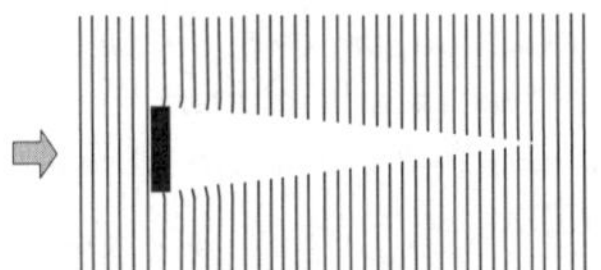

[1 mark]

When the obstacle is comparable in size to the wavelength, as it is for the long-wave radio waves, more diffraction occurs. The wavefront re-forms after a shorter distance, leaving a shorter "shadow". [1 mark]

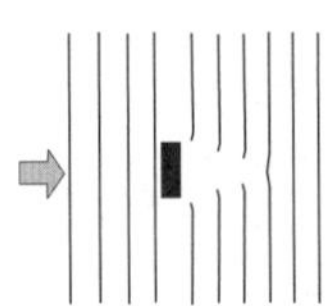

[1 mark]

Page 55 — Diffraction Gratings

1)a) Use $\sin\theta = n\lambda / d$
For the first order, $n = 1$
So, $\sin\theta = \lambda / d$ [1 mark]
No need to actually work out d. The number of lines per metre is 1 / d. So you can simply multiply the wavelength by that.
$\sin\theta = 600 \times 10^{-9} \times 4 \times 10^5 = 0.24$
$\theta = 13.9°$ [1 mark]
For the second order, $n = 2$ and $\sin\theta = 2\lambda / d$.
[1 mark]
You already have a value for λ / d. Just double it to get $\sin\theta$ for the second order.
$\sin\theta = 0.48$
$\theta = 28.7°$ [1 mark]

b) No. Putting $n = 5$ into the equation gives a value of $\sin\theta$ of 1.2, which is impossible. [1 mark]

2) $\sin\theta = n\lambda / d$, so for the 1st order maximum,
$\sin\theta = \lambda / d$ [1 mark]
$\sin 14.2° = \lambda \times 3.7 \times 10^5$
$\lambda = 663$ nm $= 6.63 \times 10^{-7}$ m
C 6.63×10^{-7} m [1 mark]

Unit 2: Section 2 — DC Electricity

Page 57 — Charge, Current and Potential Difference

1) Time in seconds = 10 × 60 = 600 s.
Use the formula $I = Q / t$ [1 mark]
which gives you $I = 4500 / 600 = 7.5$ A [1 mark]
Write down the formula first. Don't forget the unit in your answer.

2) Rearrange the formula $I = nAvq$ and you get $v = I / nAq$ [1 mark]
which gives you

$$v = \frac{13}{(1.0\times10^{29})\times(5.0\times10^{-6})\times(1.6\times10^{-19})}$$ [1 mark]

$v = 1.63 \times 10^{-4}\ \text{ms}^{-1}$ [1 mark]

3) Work done = 0.75 × electrical energy input
so the energy input will be 90 / 0.75 = 120 J. [1 mark]
Rearrange the formula $V = W / Q$ to give $Q = W / V$ [1 mark],
so you get $Q = 120 / 12 = 10$ C. [1 mark]
The electrical energy input to a motor has to be greater than the work it does because motors are less than 100% efficient.

Page 59 — Resistance and Resistivity

1) Area $= \pi(d/2)^2$ and $d = 1.0 \times 10^{-3}$ m
so Area $= \pi \times (0.5 \times 10^{-3})^2 = 7.85 \times 10^{-7}\text{m}^2$ [1 mark]

$$R = \frac{\rho l}{A} = \frac{2.8\times10^{-8}\times4}{7.85\times10^{-7}} = 0.14\ \Omega$$

[1 mark for equation or working, 1 mark for answer with unit.]

2)a) $R = V / I$ [1 mark] $= \dfrac{2}{2.67\times10^{-3}} = 749\ \Omega$ [1 mark]

b) Two further resistance calculations give 750 Ω for each answer [1 mark]
There is no significant change in resistance for different potential differences [1 mark]
Component is an ohmic conductor because its resistance is constant for different potential differences. [1 mark]

Page 61 — I/V Characteristics

1)a)

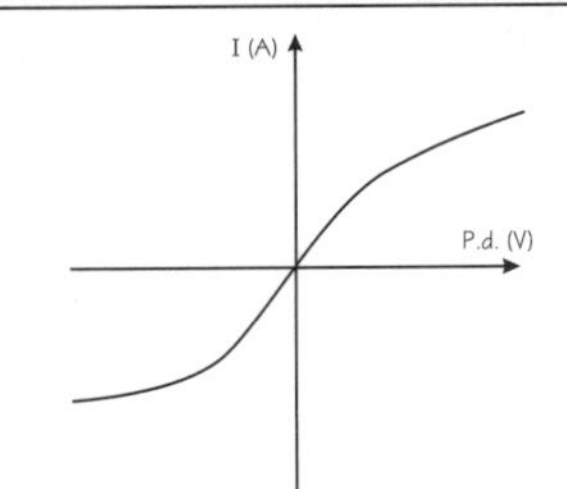

[1 mark]

b) Resistance increases as the temperature increases. [1 mark]

c) Increase in temperature makes metal ions vibrate more. [1 mark]
Increased collisions with ions impedes electrons. [1 mark]

Page 63 — Electrical Energy and Power

1)a) $I = P/V$ [1 mark] = 920/230 = 4 A [1 mark]

b) $I = V/R$ [1 mark] = 230/190 = 1.21 A [1 mark]

c) $P_{motor} = VI = 230 \times 1.21 = 278$ W [1 mark]
Total power = motor power + heater power
= 278 + 920 = 1198 W, which is approx. 1.2 kW [1 mark]

2)a) Energy supplied = $VIt = 12 \times 48 \times 2 = 1152$ J
D 1152 J [1 mark]

b) Energy lost = I^2Rt [1 mark] $= 48^2 \times 0.01 \times 2 = 46$ J
B 46 J [1 mark]

Page 65 — E.m.f. and Internal Resistance

1)a) Total resistance = $R + r = 4 + 0.8 = 4.8\ \Omega$ [1 mark]
I = e.m.f./total resistance = 24/4.8 = 5 A [1 mark]

b) $V = \varepsilon - Ir = 24 - 5 \times 0.8 = 20$ V [1 mark]

2)a) $\varepsilon = I(R + r)$, so $r = \varepsilon/I - R$ [1 mark]
$r = 500/(50 \times 10^{-3}) - 10 = 9990\ \Omega$ [1 mark]

b) This is a very high internal resistance [1 mark] so only small currents can be drawn, reducing the risk to the user [1 mark]

Answers

Page 67 — Conservation of Energy and Charge in Circuits

1)a) Resistance of parallel resistors:
$1/R_{parallel} = 1/6 + 1/3 = 1/2$
$R_{parallel} = 2\ \Omega$ [1 mark]
Total resistance:
$R_{total} = 4 + R_{parallel} = 4 + 2 = 6\ \Omega$ [1 mark]

b) $V = IR$, so rearranging $I_3 = V / R_{total}$ [1 mark]
$I_3 = 12 / 6 = 2$ A [1 mark]

c) $V = IR = 2 \times 4 = 8$ V [1 mark]

d) E.m.f. = sum of p.d.s in circuit, so $12 = 8 + V_{parallel}$
$V_{parallel} = 12 - 8 = 4$ V [1 mark]

e) Current = p.d. / resistance
$I_1 = 4 / 3 = 1.33$ A [1 mark]
$I_2 = 4 / 6 = 0.67$ A [1 mark]

Page 69 — The Potential Divider

1) Parallel circuit, so p.d. across both sets of resistors is 12 V.

i) $V_{AB} = ½ \times 12 = 6$ V [1 mark]

ii) $V_{AC} = 2/3 \times 12 = 8$ V [1 mark]

iii) $V_{BC} = V_{AC} - V_{AB} = 8 - 6 = 2$ V [1 mark]

2)a) $V_{AB} = 50/80 \times 12 = 7.5$ V [1 mark]
(ignore the 10 Ω — no current flows that way)

b) Total resistance of the parallel circuit:
$1/R_T = 1/50 + 1/(10 + 40) = 1/25$
$R_T = 25\Omega$ [1 mark]
p.d. over the whole parallel arrangement = 25/55 × 12 = 5.45 V [1 mark]
p.d. across AB = 40/50 × 5.45 = 4.36 V [1 mark]
current through 40 Ω resistor = V/R
= 4.36/40 = 0.11 A [1 mark]

Unit 2: Section 3 — The Nature of Light

Page 71 — Light — Wave or Photon

1)a) i) $E = V = 12.1$ eV [1 mark]

ii) $E = V \times 1.6 \times 10^{-19} = 12.1 \times 1.6 \times 10^{-19}$
$= 1.9 \times 10^{-18}$ J [1 mark]

b) i) The movement of an electron from a lower energy level to a higher energy level by absorbing energy. [1 mark]

ii) −13.6 + 12.1 = −1.5 eV. This corresponds to $n = 3$. [1 mark]

iii) $n = 3 \rightarrow n = 2$: 3.4 − 1.5 = 1.9 eV [1 mark]
$n = 2 \rightarrow n = 1$: 13.6 − 3.4 = 10.2 eV [1 mark]
$n = 3 \rightarrow n = 1$: 13.6 − 1.5 = 12.1 eV [1 mark]

Page 73 — The Photoelectric Effect

1) $\phi = 2.9\text{ eV} = 2.9 \times (1.6 \times 10^{-19})\text{ J} = 4.64 \times 10^{-19}\text{ J}$

$$f = \frac{\phi}{h} = \frac{4.64 \times 10^{-19}}{6.6 \times 10^{-34}} = 7.0 \times 10^{14}\text{ Hz (to 2 s.f.)}$$

D = 7.0×10^{14} Hz [1 mark]

2)a) $E = hf$ [1 mark]
$= (6.6 \times 10^{-34}) \times (2.0 \times 10^{15}) = 1.32 \times 10^{-18}$ J [1 mark]

$$1.32 \times 10^{-18}\text{ J} = \frac{1.32 \times 10^{-18}}{1.6 \times 10^{-19}}\text{ eV} = 8.25\text{ eV}$$ [1 mark]

b) $E_{max\ kinetic} = E_{photon} - \phi$ [1mark]
$= 8.25 - 4.7 = 3.55$ eV [1 mark]

3) An electron needs to gain a certain amount of energy (the work function energy) before it can leave the surface of the metal (to overcome the bonds holding it to the metal). [1 mark]
If the energy carried by each photon is less than this work function energy, no electrons will be emitted. [1 mark]

Page 75 — Light and Society

1)a) $P = \frac{E}{t} = \frac{67.2 \times 10^3}{1} = 67.2 \times 10^3$ W [1 mark]
Area = 14 × 2 × 2 = 56 m² [1 mark]

$$\text{Radiation flux} = \frac{\text{Power}}{\text{Area}} = \frac{67.2 \times 10^3}{56} = 1200\text{ Wm}^{-2}$$ [1 mark]

b) $\text{Efficiency} = \frac{\text{Useful power output}}{\text{Total power input}}$ [1 mark]

$$= \frac{12 \times 10^3}{67.2 \times 10^3} = 0.1785... \approx 18\%$$ [1 mark]

c) Any three of, e.g.
Remote sensing allows scientists to study areas that would be difficult or dangerous to go to themselves. / Remote sensing can be faster and cheaper than sending people. / Data can be recorded over long periods of time. / Remote sensing doesn't disturb the area being studied, so is unlikely to influence the data.
[1 mark for each benefit]

Index

Index